1980-20

six chord song book

Wise Publications
part of The Music Sales Group
London/New York/Sydney/Paris/Copenhagen/Berlin/Madrid/Tokyo

The *Six Chord Songbook* allows even the beginner guitarist to play and enjoy the best rock and pop tunes. With the same 6 chords used throughout the book, you'll soon master playing your favourite hits.

The *Six Chord Songbook* doesn't use music notation. Throughout the book chord boxes are printed at the head of each song; the chord changes are shown above the lyrics. It's left up to you, the guitarist, to decide on a strum rhythm or picking pattern.

You might find the pitch of the vocal line is not always comfortable because it is pitched too high or two low. In that case, you can change the key without learning a new set of chords; simply place a capo behind a suitable fret.

Whatever you do, this *Six Chord Songbook* guarantees hours of enjoyment for guitarists of all levels, as well as providing a fine basis for building a strong repertoire.

Published by:
Wise Publications,
8/9 Frith Street, London W1D 3JB, England.

Exclusive Distributors:
Music Sales Limited,
Distribution Centre, Newmarket Road,
Bury St. Edmunds, Suffolk IP33 3YB, England.
Music Sales Pty Limited,
120 Rothschild Avenue, Rosebery, NSW 2018, Australia.

Order No.AM978736
ISBN 1-84449-273-7

Compiled by Lucy Holliday.
Arranged by James Dean.
Photographs courtesy of London Features International.
Printed in the United Kingdom by
Caligraving Limited, Thetford, Norfolk.

Relative Tuning

The guitar can be tuned with the aid of pitch pipes or dedicated electronic guitar tuners which are available through your local music dealer. If you do not have a tuning device, you can use relative tuning. Estimate the pitch of the 6th string as near as possible to E or at least a comfortable pitch (not too high, as you might break other strings in tuning up). Then, while checking the various positions on the diagram, place a finger from your left hand on the:

5th fret of the E or 6th string and **tune the open A** (or 5th string) to the note (A)

5th fret of the A or 5th string and **tune the open D** (or 4th string) to the note (D)

5th fret of the D or 4th string and **tune the open G** (or 3rd string) to the note (G)

4th fret of the G or 3rd string and **tune the open B** (or 2nd string) to the note (B)

5th fret of the B or 2nd string and **tune the open E** (or 1st string) to the note (E)

E or 6th | A or 5th | D or 4th | G or 3rd | B or 2nd | E or 1st

Head

Nut

1st Fret

2nd Fret

3rd Fret

4th Fret (B)

5th Fret (A) (D) (G) (E)

Reading Chord Boxes

Chord boxes are diagrams of the guitar neck viewed head upwards, face on as illustrated. The top horizontal line is the nut, unless a higher fret number is indicated, the others are the frets.

The vertical lines are the strings, starting from E (or 6th) on the left to E (or 1st) on the right.

The black dots indicate where to place your fingers.

Strings marked with an O are played open, not fretted.
Strings marked with an X should not be played.

The curved bracket indicates a 'barre' - hold down the strings under the bracket with your first finger, using your other fingers to fret the remaining notes.

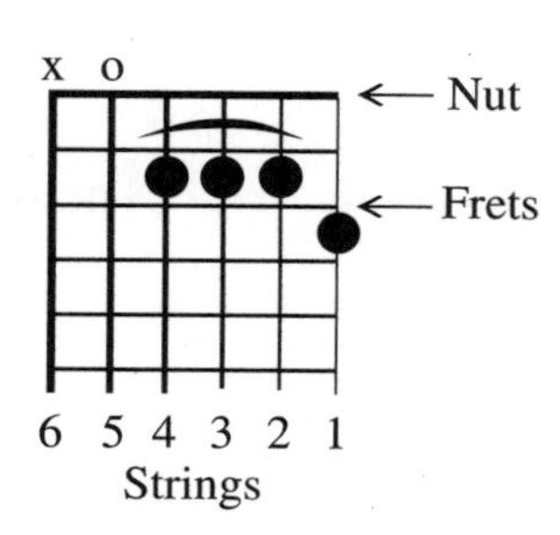

Could You Be Loved

Words & Music by
Bob Marley

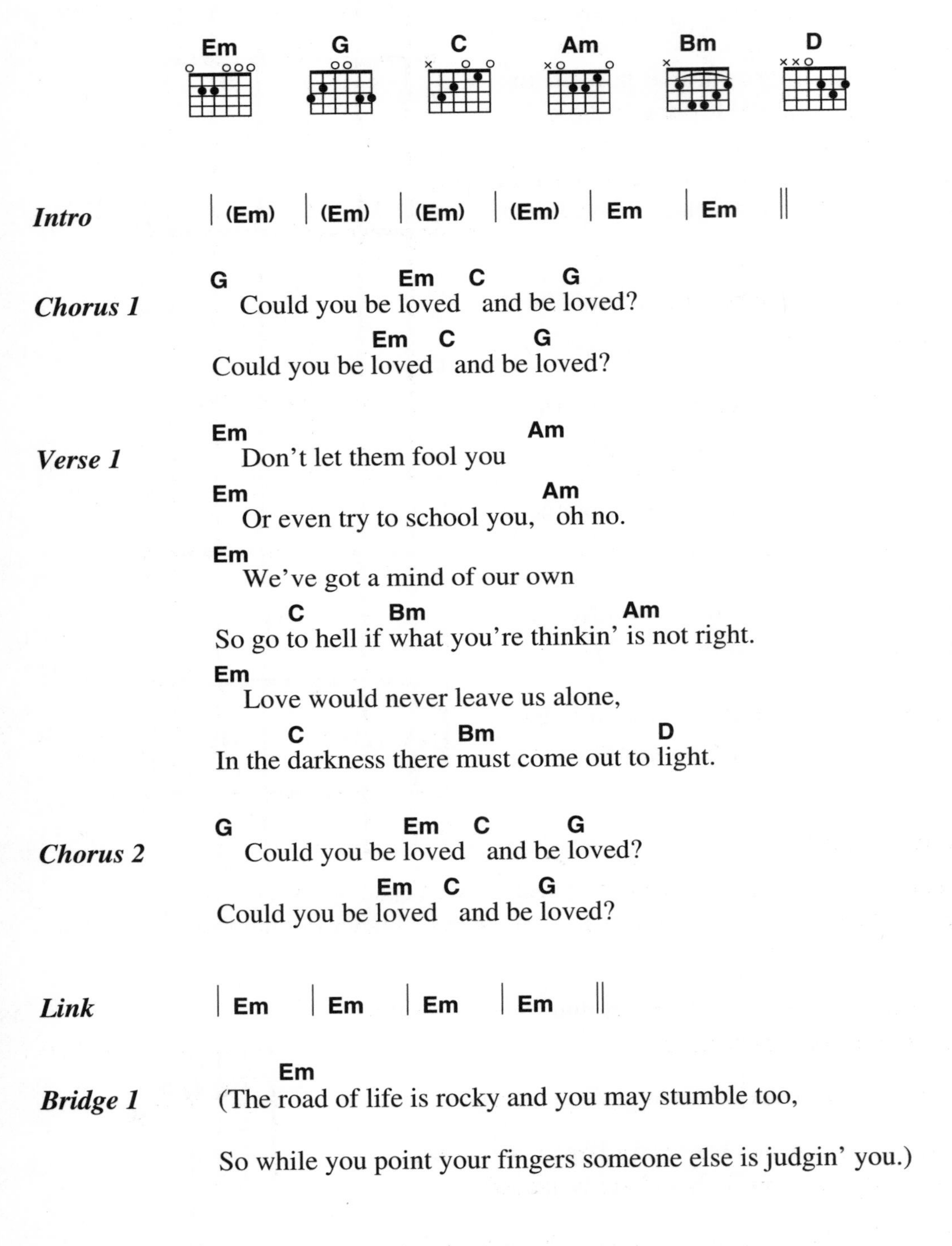

Intro | (Em) | (Em) | (Em) | (Em) | Em | Em ||

Chorus 1

G Em C G
Could you be loved and be loved?
Em C G
Could you be loved and be loved?

Verse 1

Em Am
Don't let them fool you
Em Am
Or even try to school you, oh no.
Em
We've got a mind of our own
C Bm Am
So go to hell if what you're thinkin' is not right.
Em
Love would never leave us alone,
C Bm D
In the darkness there must come out to light.

Chorus 2

G Em C G
Could you be loved and be loved?
Em C G
Could you be loved and be loved?

Link | Em | Em | Em | Em ||

Bridge 1

Em
(The road of life is rocky and you may stumble too,

So while you point your fingers someone else is judgin' you.)

cont.

```
Em
Love your brotherman.

𝄆 (Could you be, could you be, could you be loved?

Could you be, could you be loved?) 𝄇
```

Verse 2

```
Em                              Am
   Don't let them change you, oh,
Em                        Am
   Or even rearrange you,  oh no.
Em                        C    Bm   Am
   We've got a life to live (hmm-hmm-hmm).
          Em
They say   only, only
          C             Bm            D
Only the fittest of the fittest shall survive,

Stay alive.
```

Chorus 3

```
G                   Em   G      G
   Could you be loved   and be loved?
                  Em   G      G
Could you be loved   and be loved?
```

Bridge 2

```
Em
(You ain't gonna miss your water until your well runs dry,

No matter how you treat him the man will never be satisfied.

Could you be, could you be, could you be loved

Could you be, could you be loved?)
```

Coda

```
Em
(Could you be, could you be, could you be loved

Could you be, could you be loved?)

Say something, say something,

Say something, say something.

Reggae, reggae, say something.

Rockers, rockers, say something.

(Could you be loved?)  Ad lib. to fade
```

Common People

Words by Jarvis Cocker
Music by Pulp

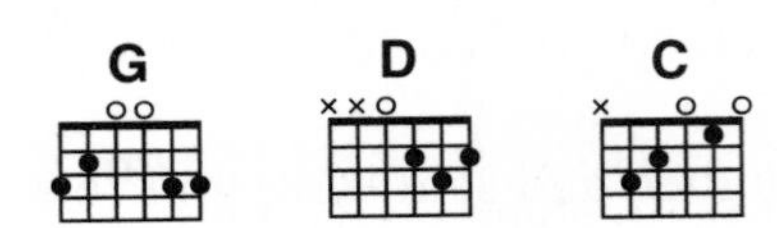

Intro | G | G | G | G ||

Verse 1

G
She came from Greece, she had a thirst for knowledge,
She studied sculpture at St. Martin's college,
D
That's where I caught her eye.
G
She told me that her dad was loaded,
I said "In that case I'll have rum and Coca Cola,"
D
She said "Fine."
And then in thirty seconds time she said
C
"I want to live like common people,
G
I want to do whatever common people do,
Want to sleep with common people,
D
I want to sleep with common people like you."
Well, what else could I do?
G
I said, "I'll - I'll see what I can do."

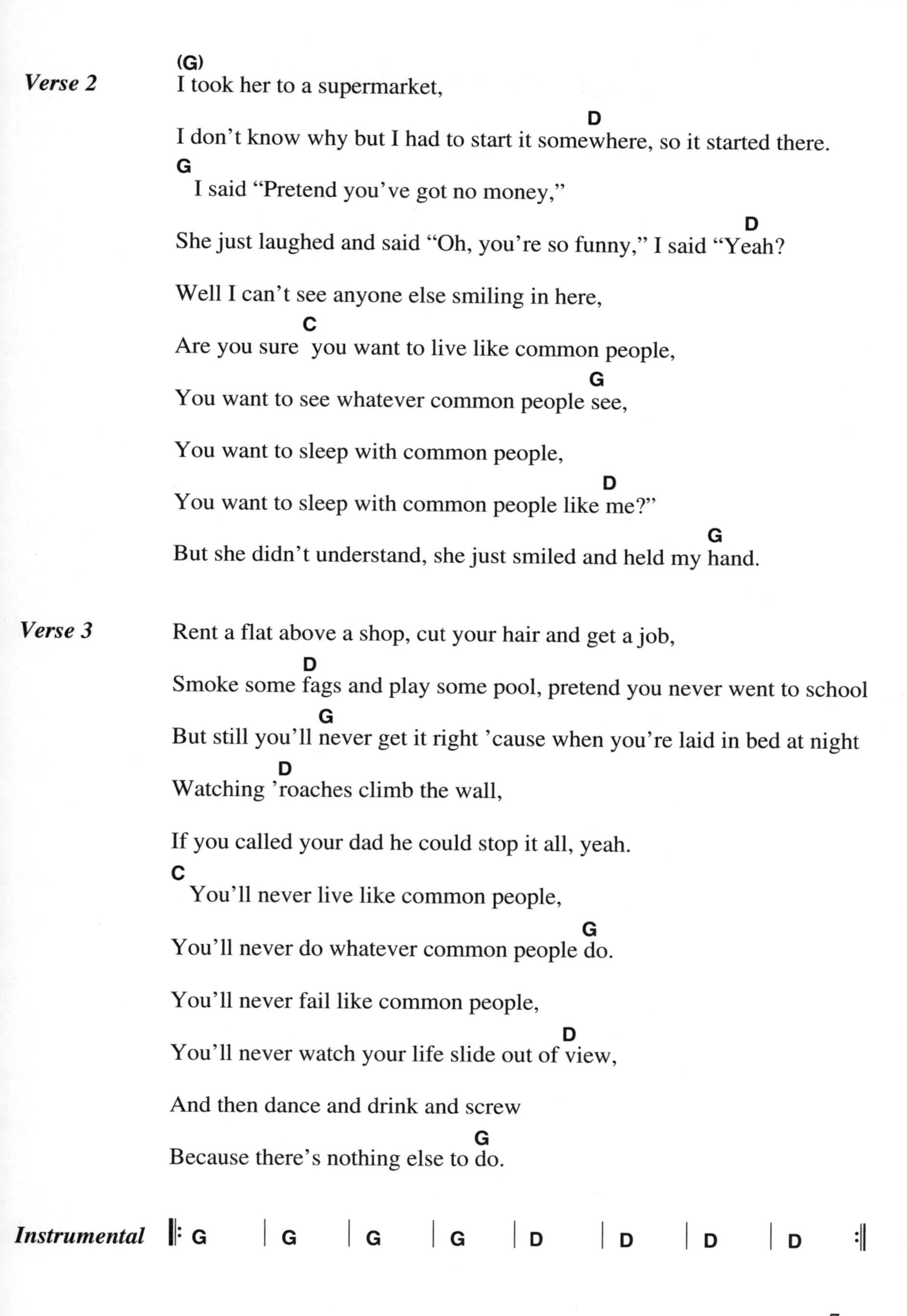

Verse 2

(G)
I took her to a supermarket,

D
I don't know why but I had to start it somewhere, so it started there.

G
I said "Pretend you've got no money,"

D
She just laughed and said "Oh, you're so funny," I said "Yeah?

Well I can't see anyone else smiling in here,

C
Are you sure you want to live like common people,

G
You want to see whatever common people see,

You want to sleep with common people,

D
You want to sleep with common people like me?"

G
But she didn't understand, she just smiled and held my hand.

Verse 3

Rent a flat above a shop, cut your hair and get a job,

D
Smoke some fags and play some pool, pretend you never went to school

G
But still you'll never get it right 'cause when you're laid in bed at night

D
Watching 'roaches climb the wall,

If you called your dad he could stop it all, yeah.

C
You'll never live like common people,

G
You'll never do whatever common people do.

You'll never fail like common people,

D
You'll never watch your life slide out of view,

And then dance and drink and screw

G
Because there's nothing else to do.

Instrumental 𝄆 G | G | G | G | D | D | D | D 𝄇

Verse 4

```
C
  Sing along with the common people,
                                 G
Sing along and it might just get you through.

Laugh along with the common people,
                                              D
Laugh along even though they're laughing at you,

And the stupid things that you do,
                              G
Because you think that poor is cool.
```

Verse 5

```
Like a dog lying in the corner,

They will bite you and never warn you,
     D
Look out, they'll tear your insides out,
G
  'Cause everybody hates a tourist,
                                        D
Especially one who thinks it's all such a laugh,

And the chip stains and grease will come out in the bath.
         C
You will never understand how it feels to live your life
        G
With no meaning or control and with nowhere left to go.
         D
You are amazed that they exist,
                                               G
And they burn so bright whilst you can only wonder why.
```

Verse 6

As Verse 3

Outro

```
| G     | G     | G     | G     ||

   (G)
||: Want to live with common people like you. :||   Play 7 times

||: Oh, la, la, la, la. :||   Play 4 times

Oh yeah.
```

Don't Panic

Words & Music by
Guy Berryman, Jon Buckland, Will Champion & Chris Martin

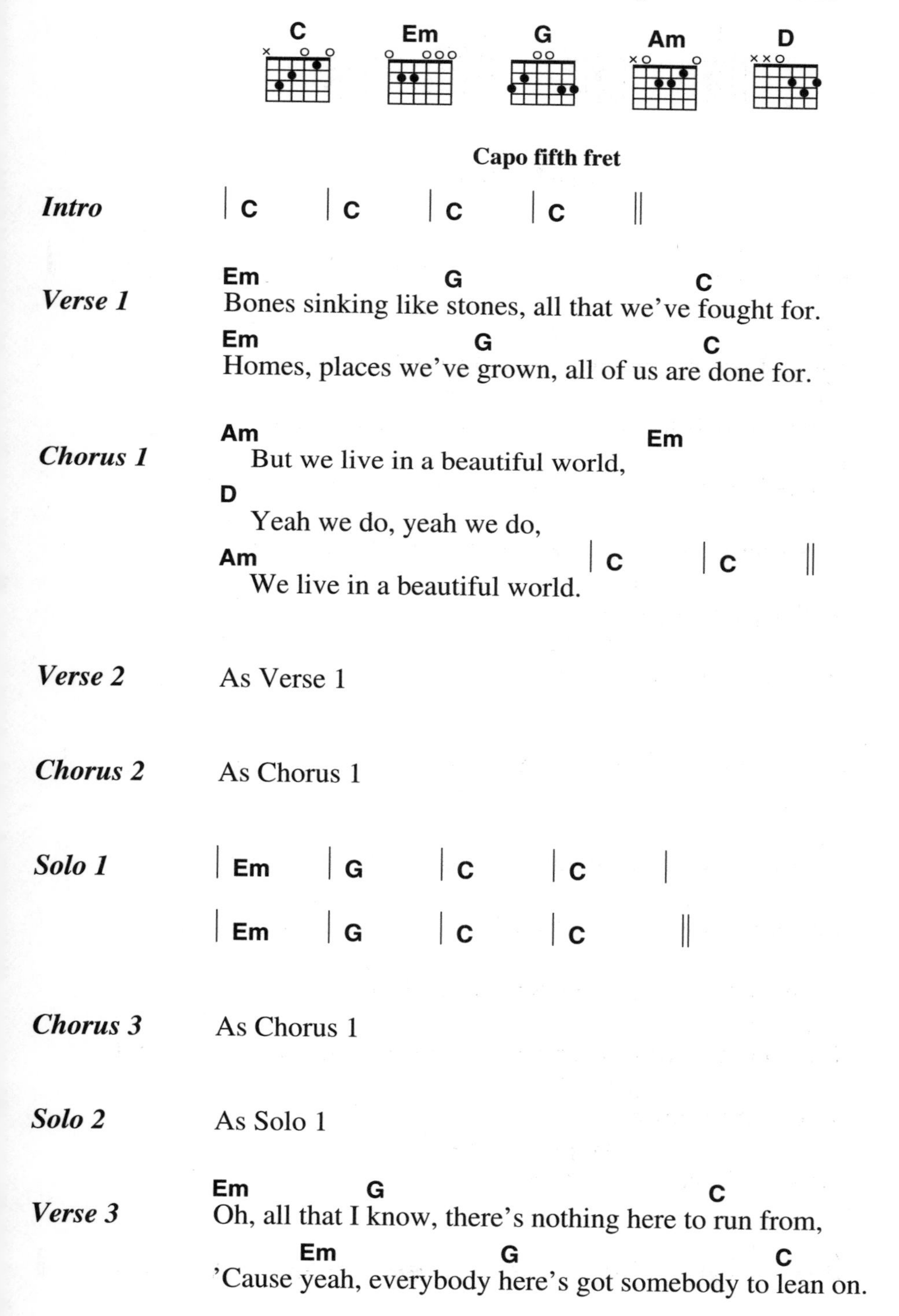

Capo fifth fret

Intro | C | C | C | C ||

Verse 1

Em G C
Bones sinking like stones, all that we've fought for.
Em G C
Homes, places we've grown, all of us are done for.

Chorus 1

Am Em
But we live in a beautiful world,
D
Yeah we do, yeah we do,
Am
We live in a beautiful world. | C | C ||

Verse 2 As Verse 1

Chorus 2 As Chorus 1

Solo 1

| Em | G | C | C |
| Em | G | C | C ||

Chorus 3 As Chorus 1

Solo 2 As Solo 1

Verse 3

Em G C
Oh, all that I know, there's nothing here to run from,
Em G C
'Cause yeah, everybody here's got somebody to lean on.

Fisherman's Blues

Words & Music by
Mike Scott & Steve Wickham

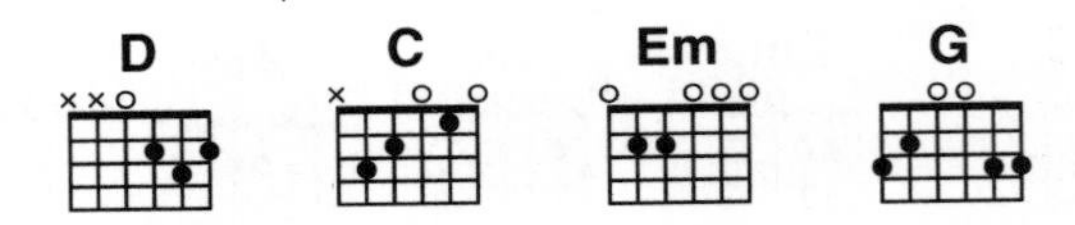

Capo fifth fret

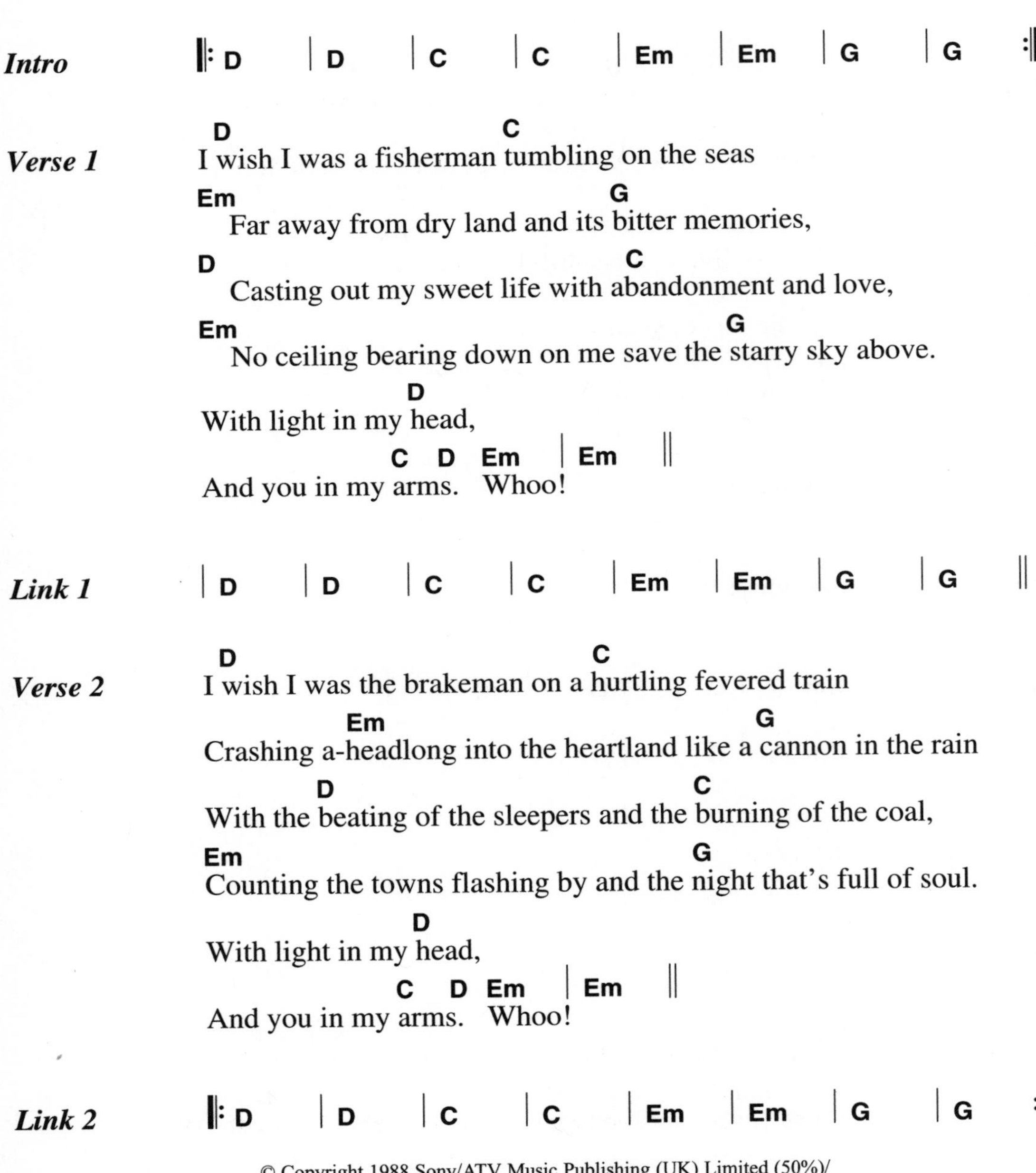

Intro |: D | D | C | C | Em | Em | G | G :|

Verse 1

D C
I wish I was a fisherman tumbling on the seas
Em G
Far away from dry land and its bitter memories,
D C
Casting out my sweet life with abandonment and love,
Em G
No ceiling bearing down on me save the starry sky above.
D
With light in my head,
C D Em | Em ||
And you in my arms. Whoo!

Link 1 | D | D | C | C | Em | Em | G | G ||

Verse 2

D C
I wish I was the brakeman on a hurtling fevered train
Em G
Crashing a-headlong into the heartland like a cannon in the rain
D C
With the beating of the sleepers and the burning of the coal,
Em G
Counting the towns flashing by and the night that's full of soul.
D
With light in my head,
C D Em | Em ||
And you in my arms. Whoo!

Link 2 |: D | D | C | C | Em | Em | G | G :|

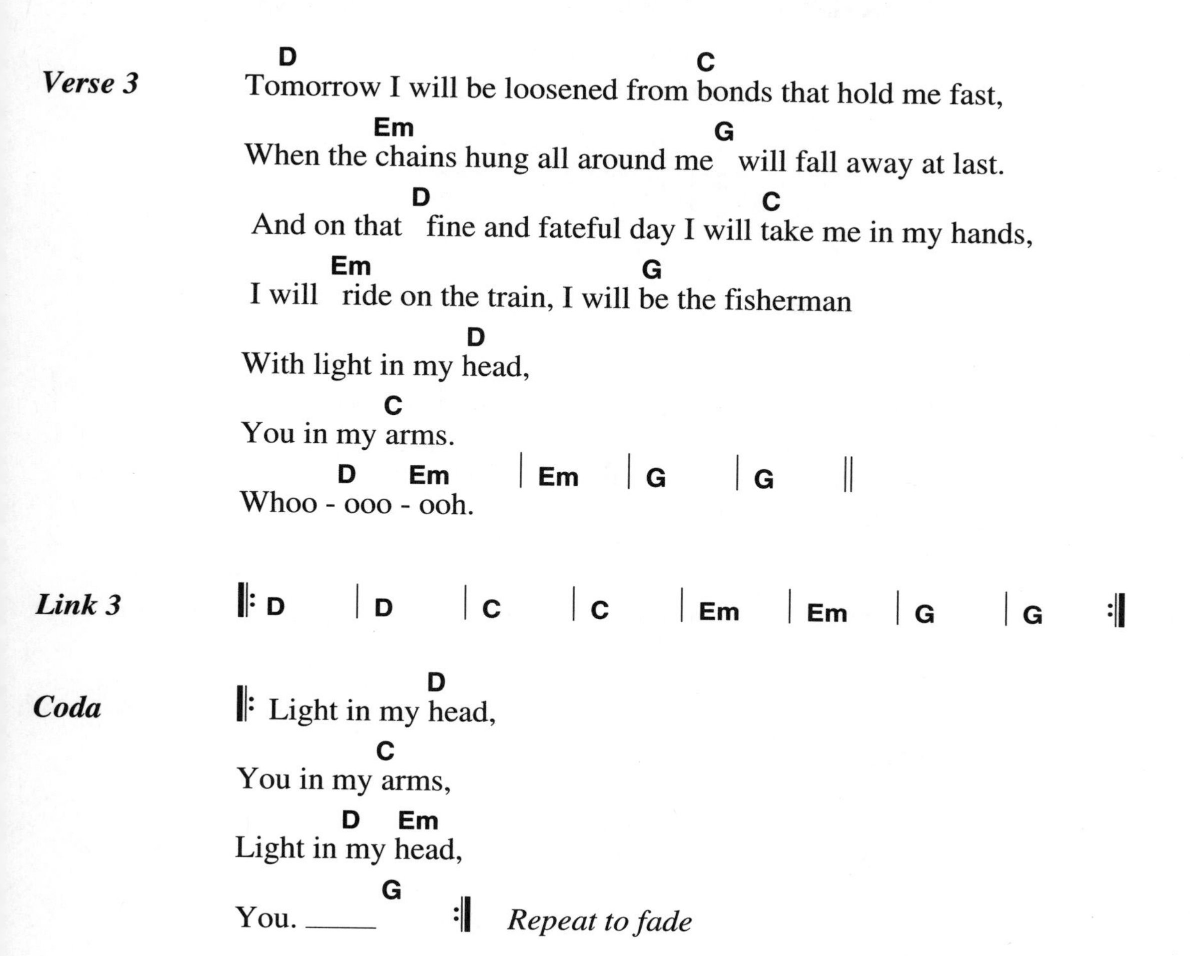

Verse 3

D C
Tomorrow I will be loosened from bonds that hold me fast,

Em G
When the chains hung all around me will fall away at last.

D C
And on that fine and fateful day I will take me in my hands,

Em G
I will ride on the train, I will be the fisherman

D
With light in my head,

C
You in my arms.

D Em | Em | G | G ||
Whoo - ooo - ooh.

Link 3

||: D | D | C | C | Em | Em | G | G :||

Coda

D
||: Light in my head,

C
You in my arms,

D Em
Light in my head,

G
You. ____ :|| *Repeat to fade*

I Love Rock N' Roll

Words & Music by
Alan Merrill & Jake Hooker

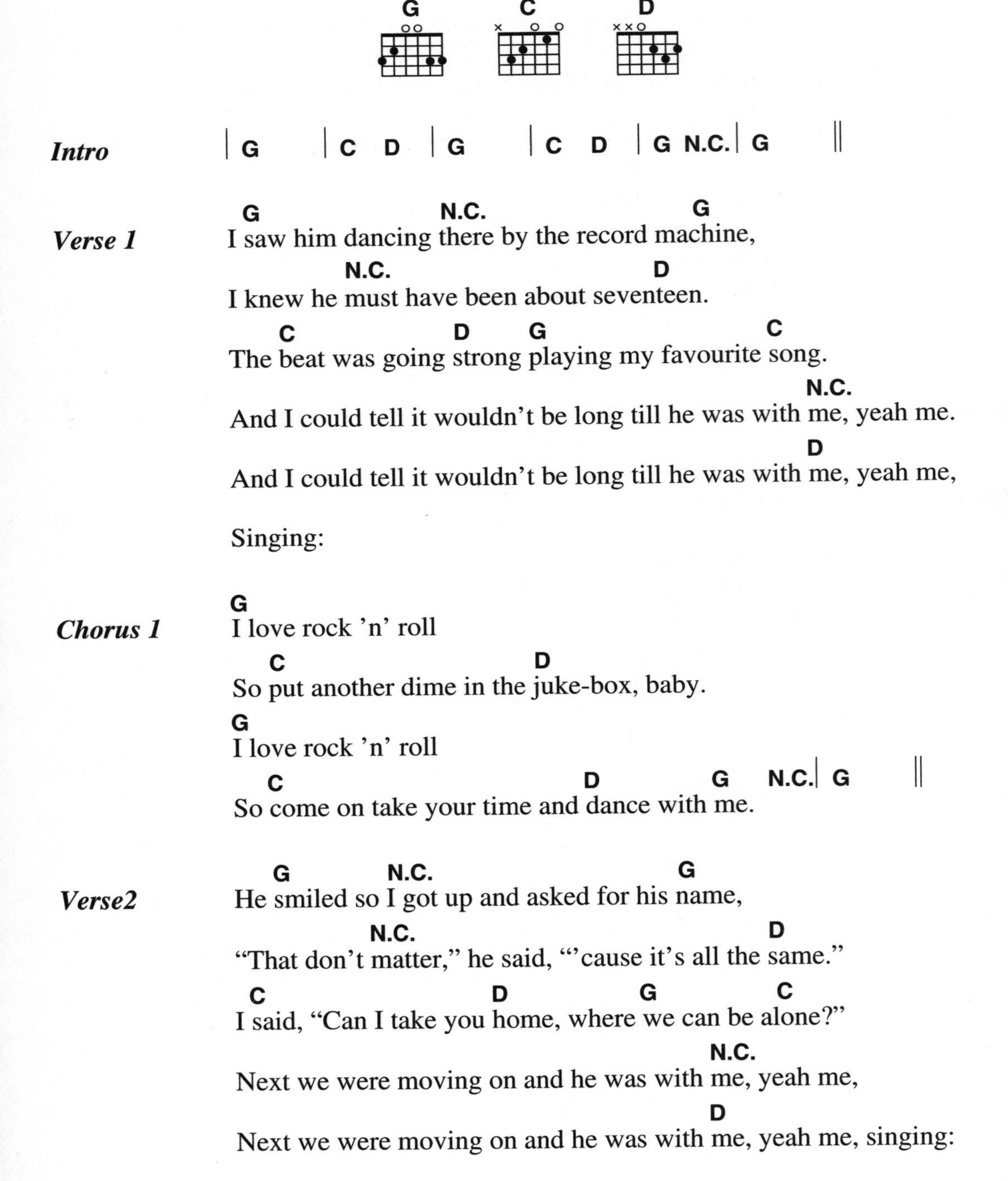


```
Intro     | G       | C   D | G       | C   D | G N.C. | G     ||

          G               N.C.              G
Verse 1   I saw him dancing there by the record machine,
                    N.C.                   D
          I knew he must have been about seventeen.
             C              D    G                  C
          The beat was going strong playing my favourite song.
                                                           N.C.
          And I could tell it wouldn't be long till he was with me, yeah me.
                                                           D
          And I could tell it wouldn't be long till he was with me, yeah me,

          Singing:

          G
Chorus 1  I love rock 'n' roll
            C                      D
          So put another dime in the juke-box, baby.
          G
          I love rock 'n' roll
            C                         D          G    N.C.| G    ||
          So come on take your time and dance with me.

            G         N.C.                G
Verse2    He smiled so I got up and asked for his name,
                       N.C.                       D
          "That don't matter," he said, "'cause it's all the same."
           C                   D            G          C
          I said, "Can I take you home, where we can be alone?"
                                                   N.C.
          Next we were moving on and he was with me, yeah me,
                                                   D
          Next we were moving on and he was with me, yeah me, singing:
```

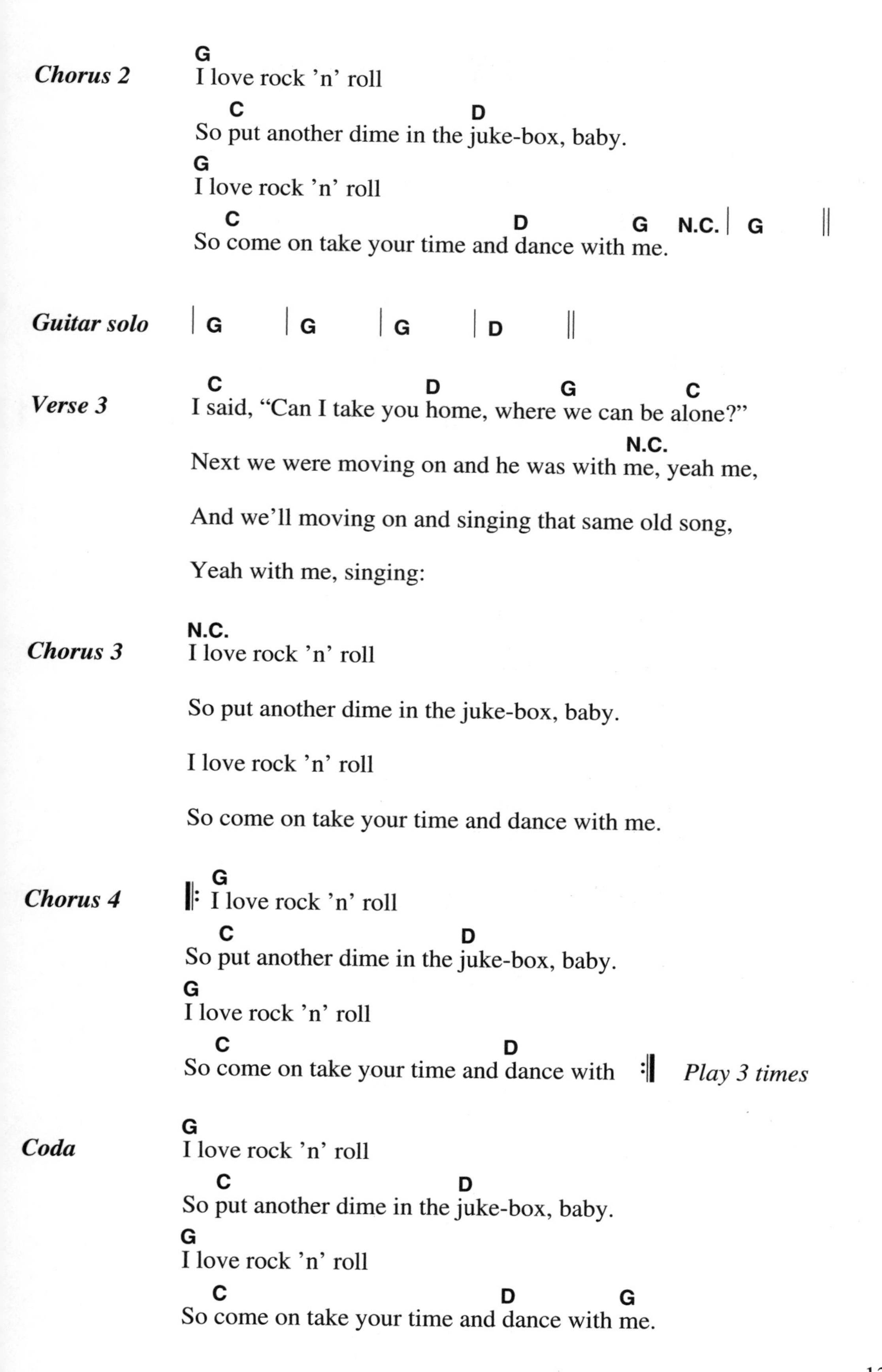

Chorus 2

G
I love rock 'n' roll
C D
So put another dime in the juke-box, baby.
G
I love rock 'n' roll
C D G N.C. | G ||
So come on take your time and dance with me.

Guitar solo

| G | G | G | D ||

Verse 3

C D G C
I said, "Can I take you home, where we can be alone?"
N.C.
Next we were moving on and he was with me, yeah me,

And we'll moving on and singing that same old song,

Yeah with me, singing:

Chorus 3

N.C.
I love rock 'n' roll

So put another dime in the juke-box, baby.

I love rock 'n' roll

So come on take your time and dance with me.

Chorus 4

G
𝄆 I love rock 'n' roll
C D
So put another dime in the juke-box, baby.
G
I love rock 'n' roll
C D
So come on take your time and dance with 𝄇 *Play 3 times*

Coda

G
I love rock 'n' roll
C D
So put another dime in the juke-box, baby.
G
I love rock 'n' roll
C D G
So come on take your time and dance with me.

In Between Days

Words & Music by
Robert Smith

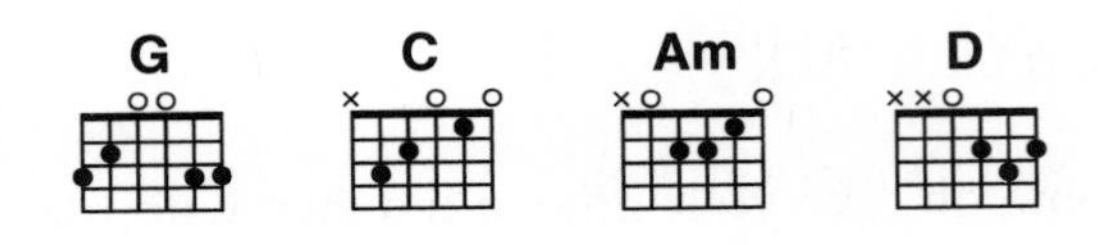

Capo second fret

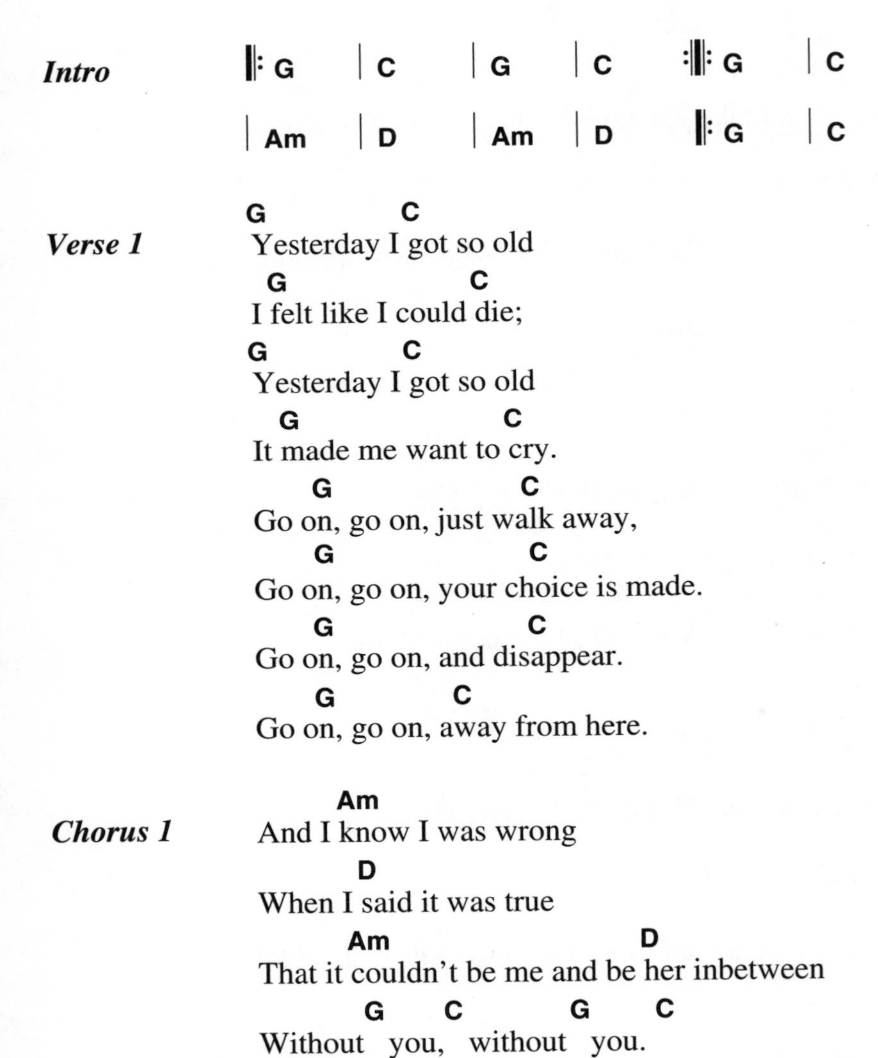

Intro ‖: G | C | G | C :‖: G | C | G | C :‖
| Am | D | Am | D ‖: G | C | G | C :‖

Verse 1
```
G                C
Yesterday I got so old
  G                  C
I felt like I could die;
G                C
Yesterday I got so old
   G                   C
It made me want to cry.
      G                    C
Go on, go on, just walk away,
      G                    C
Go on, go on, your choice is made.
      G                    C
Go on, go on, and disappear.
      G             C
Go on, go on, away from here.
```

Chorus 1
```
         Am
And I know I was wrong
          D
When I said it was true
         Am                              D
That it couldn't be me and be her inbetween
          G     C        G      C
Without  you,  without  you.
```

Link | G | C | G | C ‖

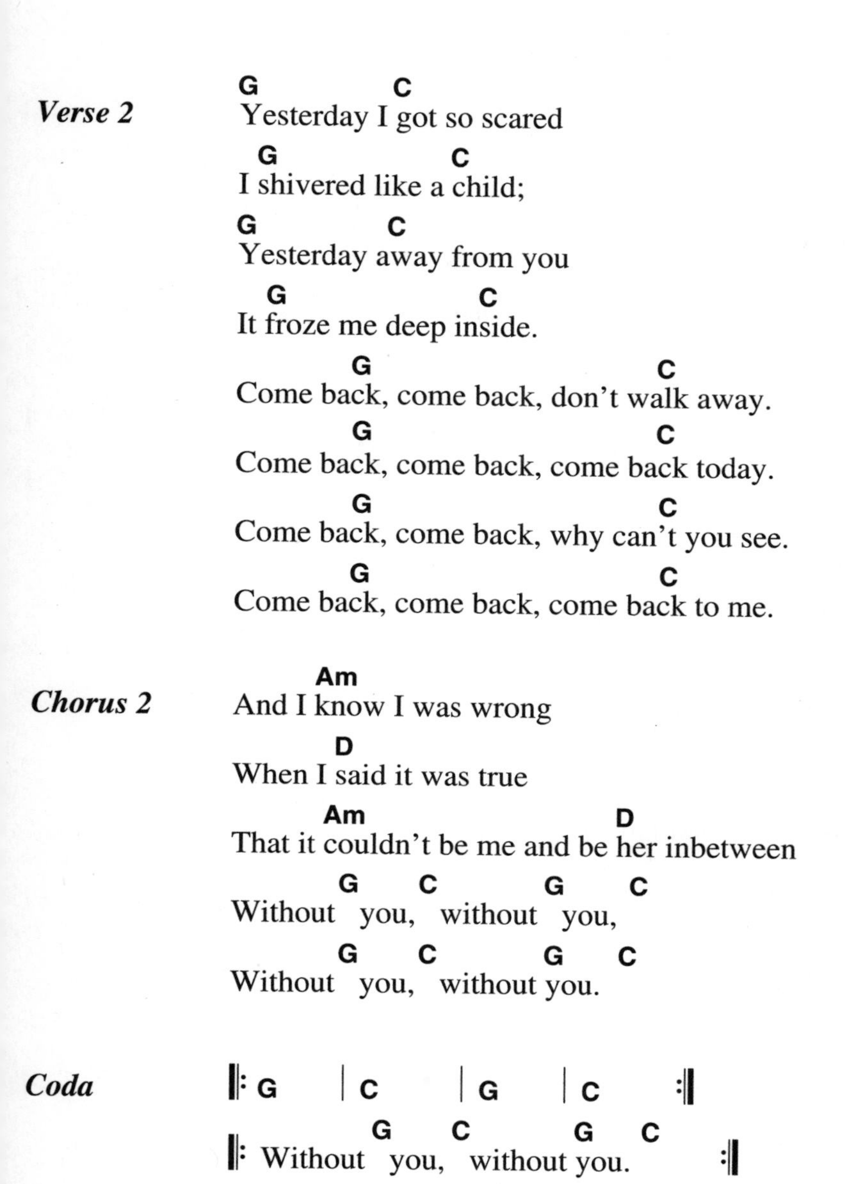
Verse 2
G C
Yesterday I got so scared
G C
I shivered like a child;
G C
Yesterday away from you
G C
It froze me deep inside.
G C
Come back, come back, don't walk away.
G C
Come back, come back, come back today.
G C
Come back, come back, why can't you see.
G C
Come back, come back, come back to me.
Chorus 2
Am
And I know I was wrong
D
When I said it was true
Am D
That it couldn't be me and be her inbetween
G C G C
Without you, without you,
G C G C
Without you, without you.
Coda
𝄆 G | C | G | C 𝄇
G C G C
𝄆 Without you, without you. 𝄇

Luka

Words & Music by
Suzanne Vega

G D C Em

Tune guitar down one semitone

Intro | G | D | C | D |
||: Em | D :||: C | D :||

Verse 1
G D
My name is Luka,
C D
I live on the second floor,
G D
I live upstairs from you
C D
Yes I think you've seen me before.
Em D
If you hear something late at night
Em D
Some kind of trouble
C
Some kind of fight,
D
Just don't ask me what it was,
C D
Just don't ask me what it was,
C D
Just don't ask me what it was.

Verse 2
G D
I think it's 'cause I'm clumsy,
C D
I try not to talk too loud,
G D
Maybe it's because I'm crazy,
C D
I try not to act too proud.
Em D Em
They only hit until you cry,

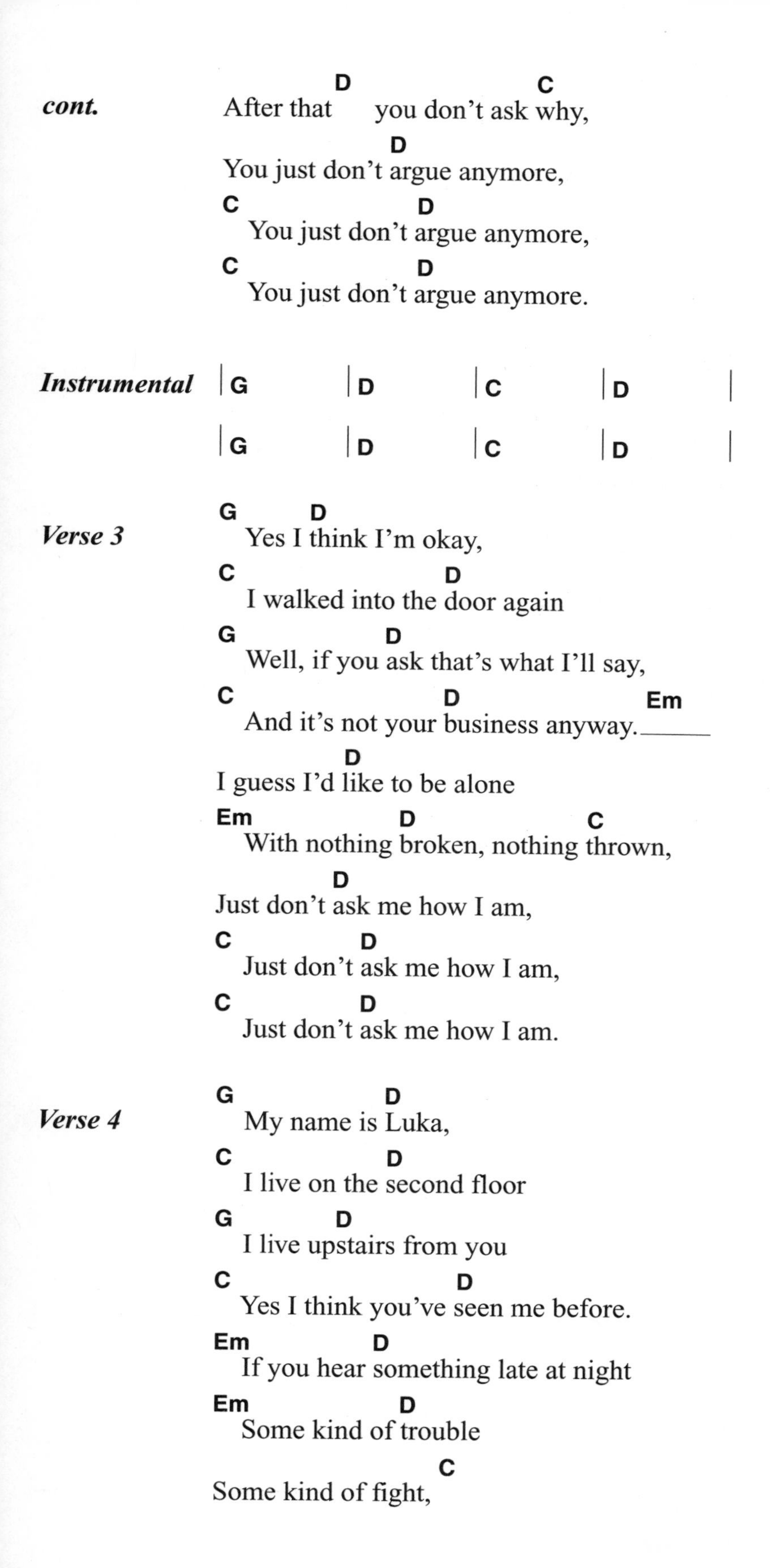

cont.

```
            D                   C
After that      you don't ask why,
                    D
You just don't argue anymore,
C                       D
   You just don't argue anymore,
C                       D
   You just don't argue anymore.
```

Instrumental

```
| G        | D        | C        | D        |
| G        | D        | C        | D        |
```

Verse 3

```
G        D
   Yes I think I'm okay,
C                         D
   I walked into the door again
G                    D
   Well, if you ask that's what I'll say,
C                            D                 Em
   And it's not your business anyway.______
                  D
I guess I'd like to be alone
Em                      D                C
   With nothing broken, nothing thrown,
                D
Just don't ask me how I am,
C                  D
   Just don't ask me how I am,
C                  D
   Just don't ask me how I am.
```

Verse 4

```
G                   D
   My name is Luka,
C                    D
   I live on the second floor
G              D
   I live upstairs from you
C                            D
   Yes I think you've seen me before.
Em                   D
   If you hear something late at night
Em                    D
   Some kind of trouble
                         C
Some kind of fight,
```

cont.

```
                 D
Just don't ask me what it was,
C                D
   Just don't ask me what it was,
C                D
   Just don't ask me what it was.
Em                 D                Em
   They only hit       until you cry
                  D                C
And after that       you don't ask why
                   D
You just don't argue anymore,
C                   D
   You just don't argue anymore,
C                   D
   You just don't argue anymore.
```

Outro

```
| G      | D      | C      | D      |
| G      | D      | C      | D      |
| Em     | D      | C      | D      |
| G      ||
```

Nothing Ever Happens

Words & Music by
Justin Currie

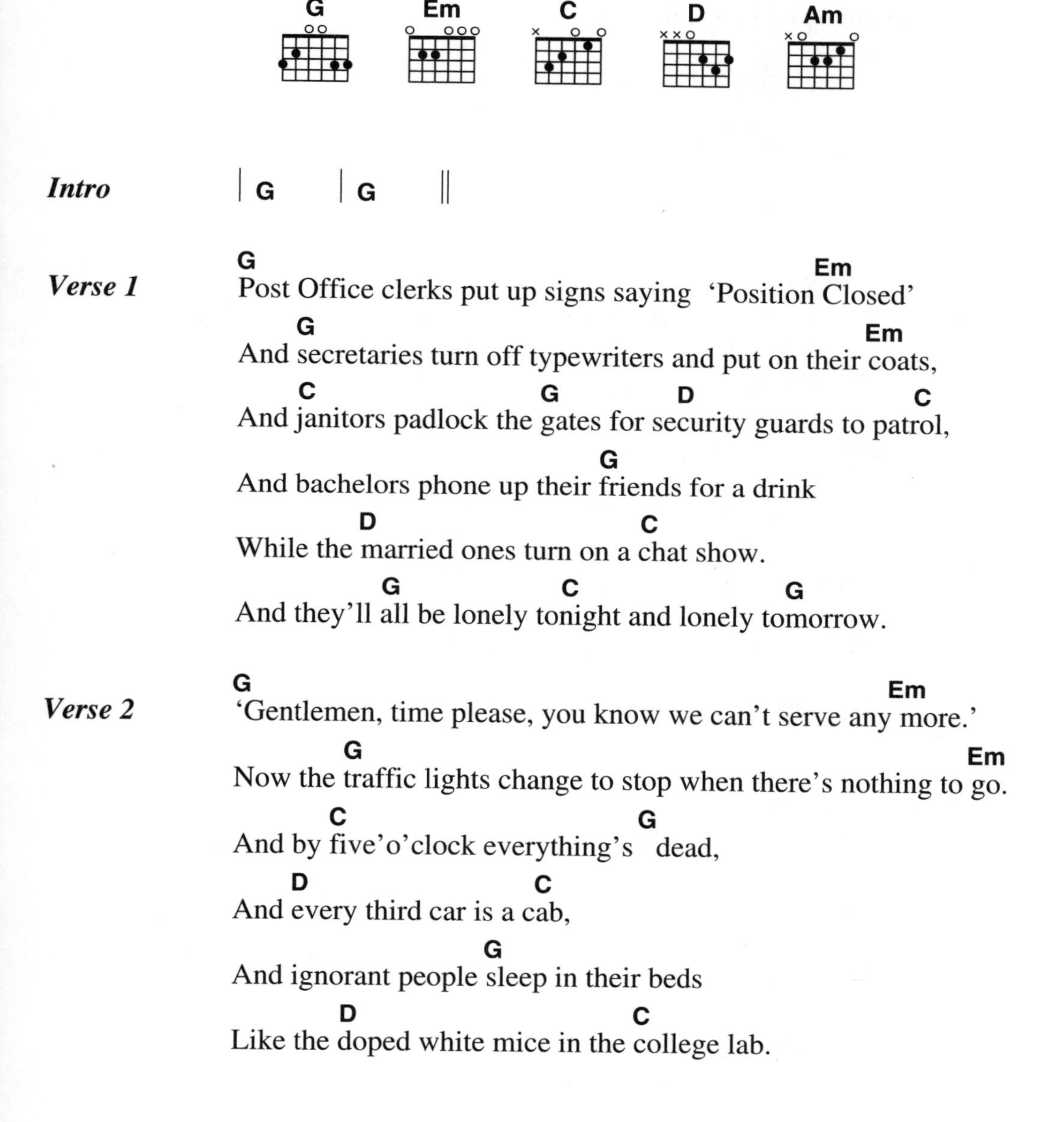

Intro | G | G ||

Verse 1

G Em
Post Office clerks put up signs saying 'Position Closed'
G Em
And secretaries turn off typewriters and put on their coats,
C G D C
And janitors padlock the gates for security guards to patrol,
G
And bachelors phone up their friends for a drink
D C
While the married ones turn on a chat show.
G C G
And they'll all be lonely tonight and lonely tomorrow.

Verse 2

G Em
'Gentlemen, time please, you know we can't serve any more.'
G Em
Now the traffic lights change to stop when there's nothing to go.
C G
And by five'o'clock everything's dead,
D C
And every third car is a cab,
G
And ignorant people sleep in their beds
D C
Like the doped white mice in the college lab.

Chorus 1

```
   G              C
And nothing ever happens,
G                     C
   Nothing happens at all:
   Am                      C
The needle returns to the start of the song
         D                  C
And we all sing along like before,
           G          C
And we'll all be lonely tonight
             G
And lonely tomorrow.
```

Verse 3

```
   G                                                D       Em
The telephone exchanges click while there's nobody there.
   G
The Martians could land in the car park
                  Em
And no-one could care.
   C                         G
The close-circuit cameras in department stores
         D                C
Shoot the same movie everyday
                                       G
And the stars of these films neither die nor get killed,
        D                          C      G   Am  D
Just survive constant action replay.
```

Chorus 2

As Chorus 1

Verse 4

```
   G                                                   Em
And bill hoardings advertise products that nobody needs,
       G
While 'Angry from Manchester' writes
                   Em
To complain about all the repeats on TV;
```

cont.

```
     C                  G
And computer terminals report
                   D                    C
Some gains in the values of copper and tin,
                           G
While American businessmen snap up Van Goghs
         D                  C       G    Am  D
For the price of a hospital wing.
```

Chorus 3

```
     G           C
And nothing ever happens,
G                      C
  Nothing happens at all:
      Am                   C
The needle returns to the start of the song
          D                   C
And we all sing along like before.
     G           C
And nothing ever happens,
G                      C
  Nothing happens at all:
         Am                         C
They'll burn down the synagogues at six o'clock,
           D                   C
And we'll all go along like before,
            G             C
And we'll all be lonely tonight
             G
And lonely tomorrow.
```

Perfect 10

Words & Music by
Paul Heaton & David Rotheray

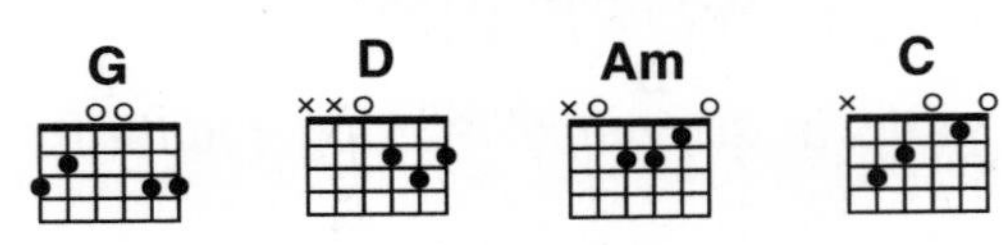

Intro 𝄆 G | G | G | D 𝄇

Verse 1

```
G
  She's a perfect ten,
But she wears a twelve,
                                D
Baby keep a little two for me.
G
  She could be sweet sixteen,
Busting out of the seams,
                                D
It's still love in the first degree.
G
  When he's at my gate,
With a big fat eight,
                                      D
You wanna see the smile on my face.
G
  And even at my door,
With a poor, poor four,
                               D
There ain't no man can replace.
```

Chorus 1

```
                      G                    Am
'Cause we love our love in different sizes,
            D                    G
I love her body especially the lines.
                                     Am
Time takes it's toll but not on the eyes,
              D               G
Promise me this, take me tonight.
```

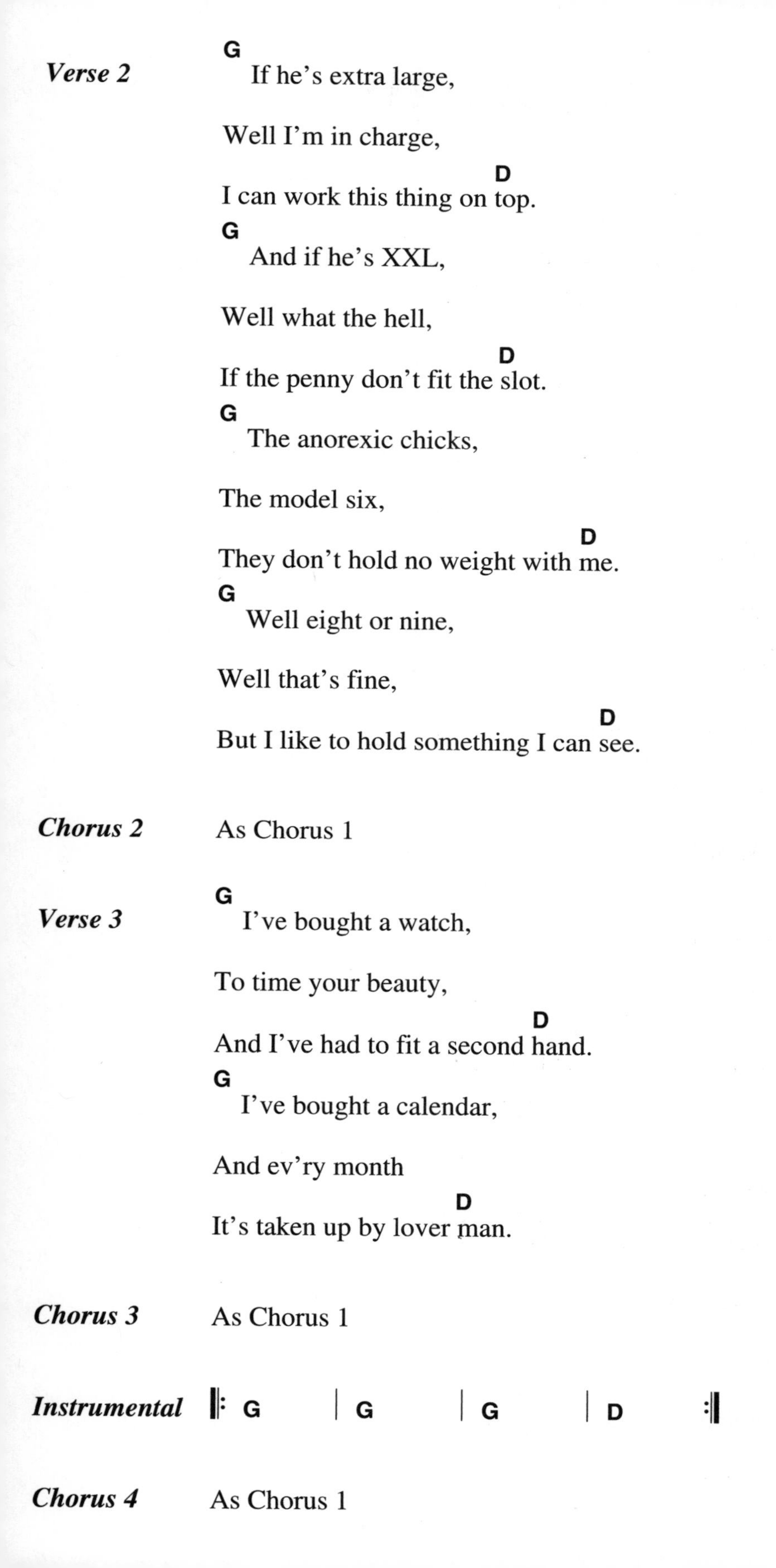

Verse 2

```
G
  If he's extra large,
Well I'm in charge,
                        D
I can work this thing on top.
G
  And if he's XXL,
Well what the hell,
                         D
If the penny don't fit the slot.
G
  The anorexic chicks,
The model six,
                                D
They don't hold no weight with me.
G
  Well eight or nine,
Well that's fine,
                                  D
But I like to hold something I can see.
```

Chorus 2 As Chorus 1

Verse 3

```
G
  I've bought a watch,
To time your beauty,
                             D
And I've had to fit a second hand.
G
  I've bought a calendar,
And ev'ry month
                          D
It's taken up by lover man.
```

Chorus 3 As Chorus 1

Instrumental ‖: G | G | G | D :‖

Chorus 4 As Chorus 1

Sail Away

Words & Music by
David Gray

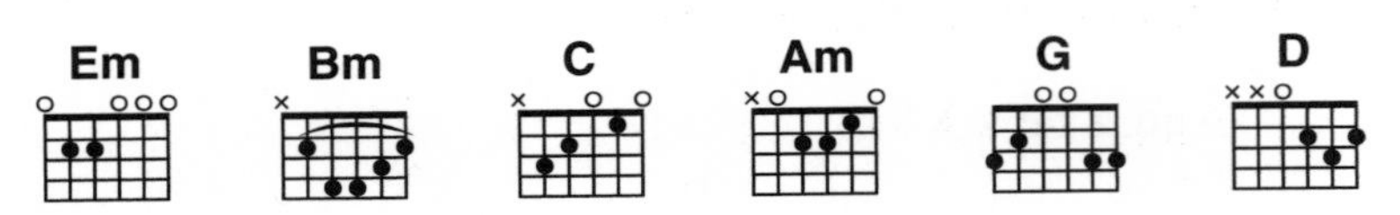

Capo fourth fret

Intro | Em | Em | Em | Em ||

Chorus 1

```
Em
  Sail away with me honey,
Bm
  I put my heart in your hands.
Em                          C     Am
  Sail away with me honey now, now, now.
Em      G
  Sail away with me,
C              Am
  What will be will be,
C                      D     Am
  I wanna hold you now, now, now. __
```

Verse 1

```
G                         Bm
  Crazy skies all wild above me now,
G                          Bm
  Winter howling at my face.
G                    Bm
  And everything I held so dear
Em                         D
  Disappeared without a trace.
G                                Bm
  Though all the times I've tasted love,
G                                Bm
  Never knew quite what I had.
G                           Bm
  Little darling if you hear me now,
Em                         D
  Never needed you so bad.
C                               Am
  Spinning 'round inside my head.
```

Chorus 2 As Chorus 1

Verse 2

```
G                           Bm
  I've been talking drunken gibberish
G                    Bm
  Falling in and out of bars,
G                      Bm
  Trying to get some explanation here
Em                           D
  For the way some people are;
C                      Am
  How did it ever come so far?
```

Chorus 3 As Chorus 1

Chorus 4 As Chorus 1

Chorus 4

```
Em
  Sail away with me honey,
Bm
  I put my heart in your hands.
Em                                     C           Am
  You'll break me up if you put me down, woh. ___
Em        G
  Sail away with me,
C             Am
  What will be will be.
C                      D    Am
  I wanna hold you now, now, now.
```

Coda

Em	Bm	Em	C Am
Em G	C Am	C	D Am
Em	Em	Em	Em ‖

Sit Down

Words & Music by
Tim Booth, Larry Gott, Jim Glennie & Gavan Whelan

G C D

Intro ‖: G | G | C | D :‖

Verse 1

G C D
I'll sing myself to sleep, a song from the darkest hour.
G C D
Secret's I can't keep inside all the day.
G C D
Swing from high to deep, extremes of sweet and sour.
G C D
Hope that God exists, I hope, I pray.

Bridge

G
Drawn by the undertow,
C D
My life is out of control.
G C
I believe this wave will bear my weight,
D
So let it flow.

Chorus 1

G
Oh sit down, oh sit down, oh sit down,
C D
Sit down next to me.
G
Sit down, down, down, down,
C D
Down in sympathy.

Instrumental ‖: G | G | C | D :‖

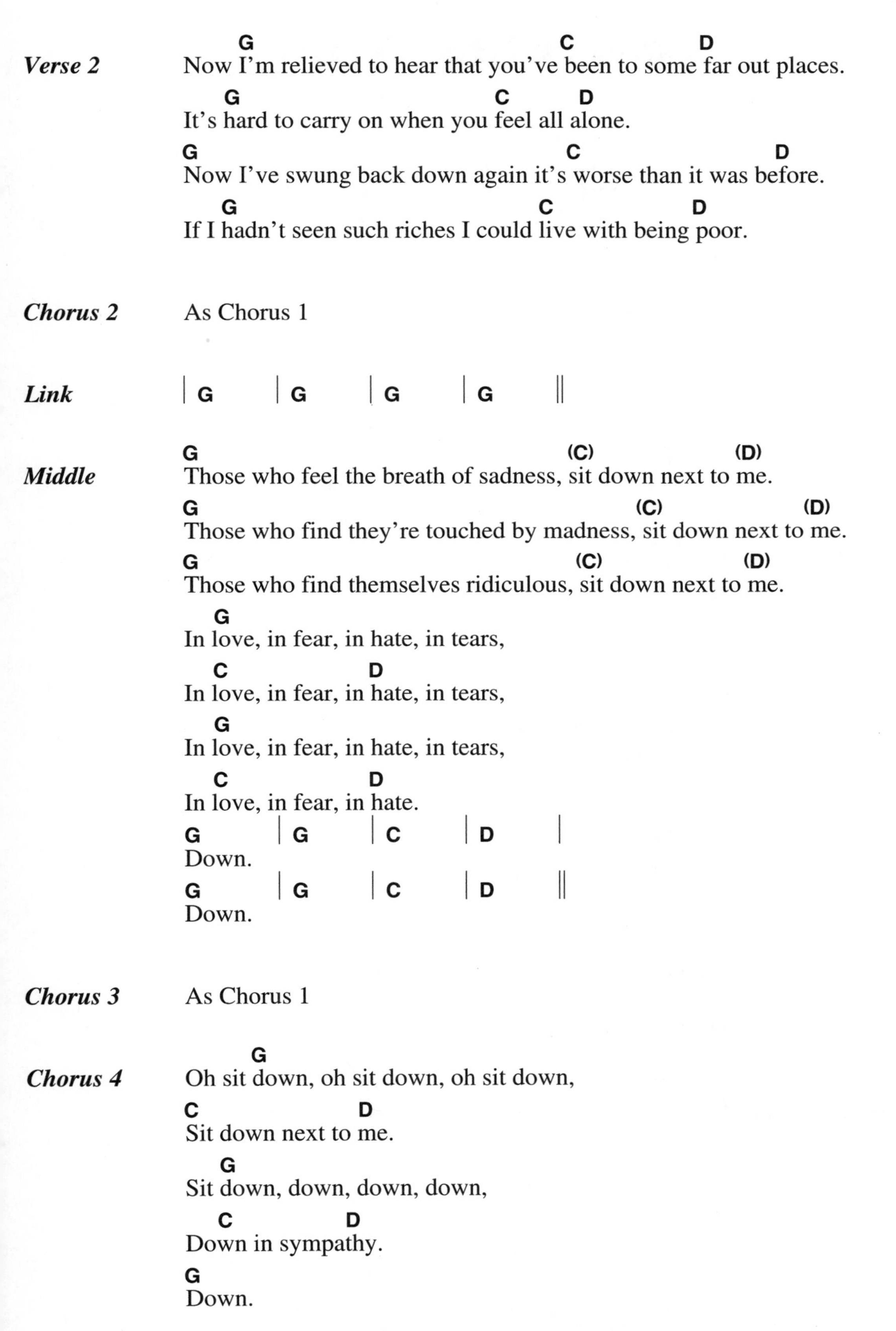

Verse 2

G C D
Now I'm relieved to hear that you've been to some far out places.
G C D
It's hard to carry on when you feel all alone.
G C D
Now I've swung back down again it's worse than it was before.
G C D
If I hadn't seen such riches I could live with being poor.

Chorus 2

As Chorus 1

Link

| G | G | G | G ||

Middle

G (C) (D)
Those who feel the breath of sadness, sit down next to me.
G (C) (D)
Those who find they're touched by madness, sit down next to me.
G (C) (D)
Those who find themselves ridiculous, sit down next to me.
G
In love, in fear, in hate, in tears,
C D
In love, in fear, in hate, in tears,
G
In love, in fear, in hate, in tears,
C D
In love, in fear, in hate.
G | G | C | D |
Down.
G | G | C | D ||
Down.

Chorus 3

As Chorus 1

Chorus 4

G
Oh sit down, oh sit down, oh sit down,
C D
Sit down next to me.
G
Sit down, down, down, down,
C D
Down in sympathy.
G
Down.

Sweetest Thing

Words & Music by
U2

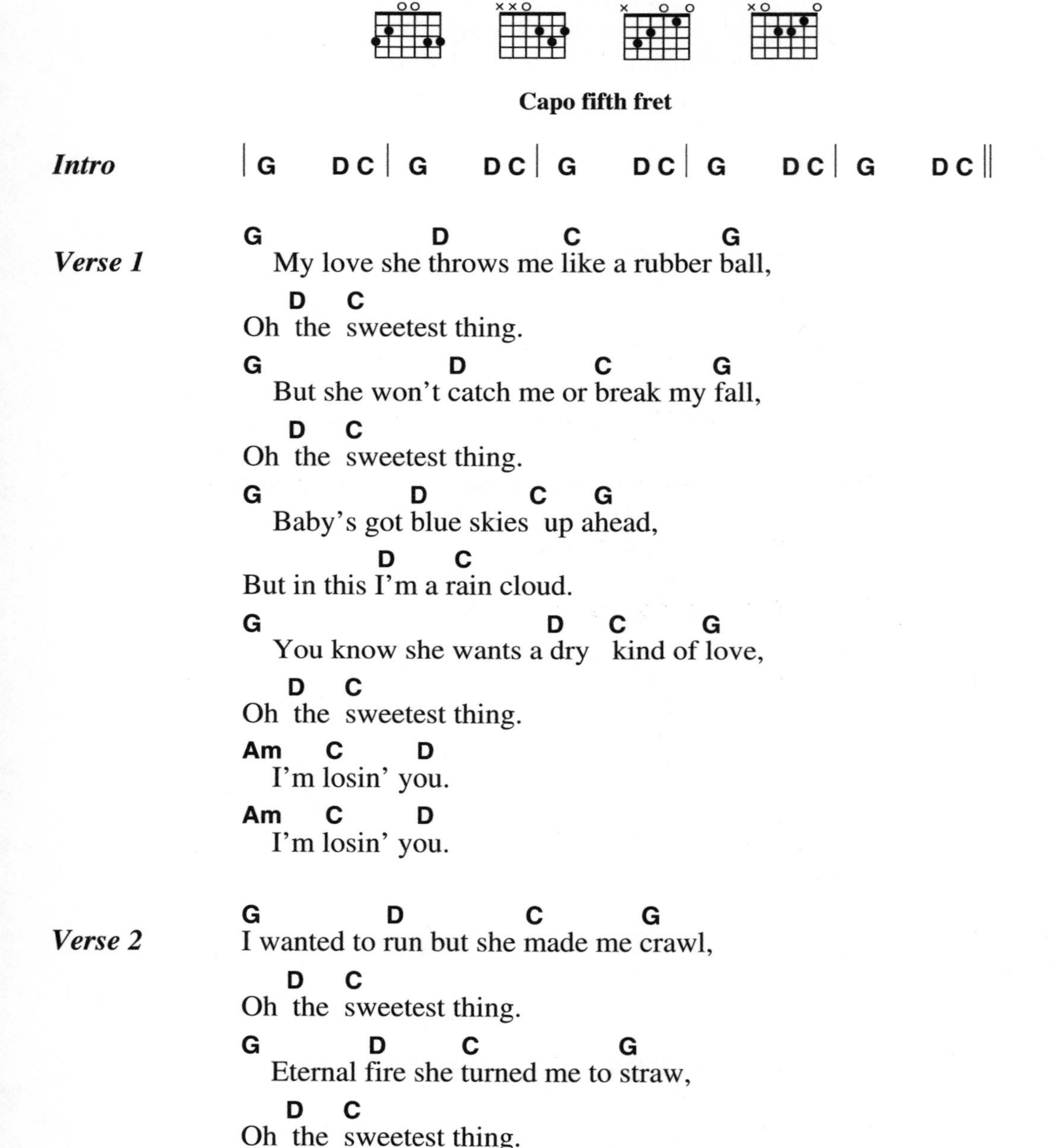

Capo fifth fret

Intro | G D C | G D C | G D C | G D C | G D C ||

Verse 1

```
G                  D            C              G
   My love she throws me like a rubber ball,
   D     C
Oh  the  sweetest thing.
G                   D             C           G
   But she won't catch me or break my fall,
   D     C
Oh  the  sweetest thing.
G                 D              C     G
   Baby's got blue skies  up ahead,
                D        C
But in this I'm a rain cloud.
G                                  D     C       G
   You know she wants a dry   kind of love,
   D     C
Oh  the  sweetest thing.
Am      C          D
   I'm losin'  you.
Am      C          D
   I'm losin'  you.
```

Verse 2

```
G                 D                 C             G
I wanted to run but she made me crawl,
   D     C
Oh  the  sweetest thing.
G              D          C              G
   Eternal fire she turned me to straw,
   D     C
Oh  the  sweetest thing.
```

```
cont.          G                 D     C
                 I know I got black eyes,
                          G         D             C
               But they burn so brightly for her.
               G                 D     C       G
                 I guess it's a blind kind of love.
                  D   C
               Oh the sweetest thing.
               Bm    C     D
                 I'm losin' you, whoa,
               Bm   C           D
               I'm  losin' you.
                                      C
               Ain't love the sweetest thing?

               Ain't love the sweetest thing?


Instrumental   ||: G    D C | G    D C | G    D C :||


Verse 3        G              D      C            G
                 Blue eyed boy to brown eyed girl,
                  D   C
               Oh the sweetest thing.
               G                 D           C           G
                 You can set it up, but you still see the tear,
                  D   C
               Oh the sweetest thing.
               G               D           C  G
                 Baby's got blue skies up ahead,
                             D      C
               But in this I'm a rain cloud,
               G             D       C      G
                 Ours is a stormy kind of love,
                  D   C
               Oh the sweetest thing.


                 G              C
Outro          ||: Do do do do, do do do do,
               G              C
               Do, do do do do do do do.      :||
               G              C
               Do do do do, do the sweetest thing.
               G              C                     G
               Do do do do, do the sweetest thing.
```

Ten Storey Love Song

Words & Music by
John Squire

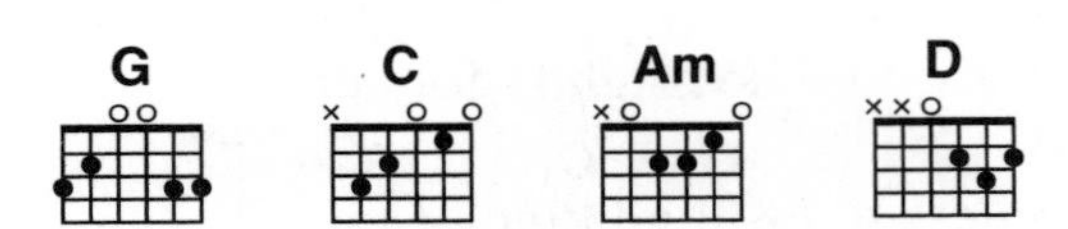

Intro ‖: G :‖ *Ad lib.*

Verse 1

```
                G                  C
When your heart is black and broken
           G               C
And you need a helping hand,
              G           Am
When you're so much in love
            G          C               D
You don't know just how much you can stand.
                G                C
When your questions go unanswered
           G             C
And the silence is killing you,
           G           Am
Take my hand, baby, I'm your man,
           C        G        D          | D     ||
I've got loving enough for two.
```

Chorus 1

```
G     C    G
Ten storey love song,
 C         G        Am
I built this thing for you.
G         C        G
Who can take you higher
       C       G          Am
Than twin peak mountain blue?
             C        G         Am
Oh well, I built this thing for you,
       D
And I love you true.
```

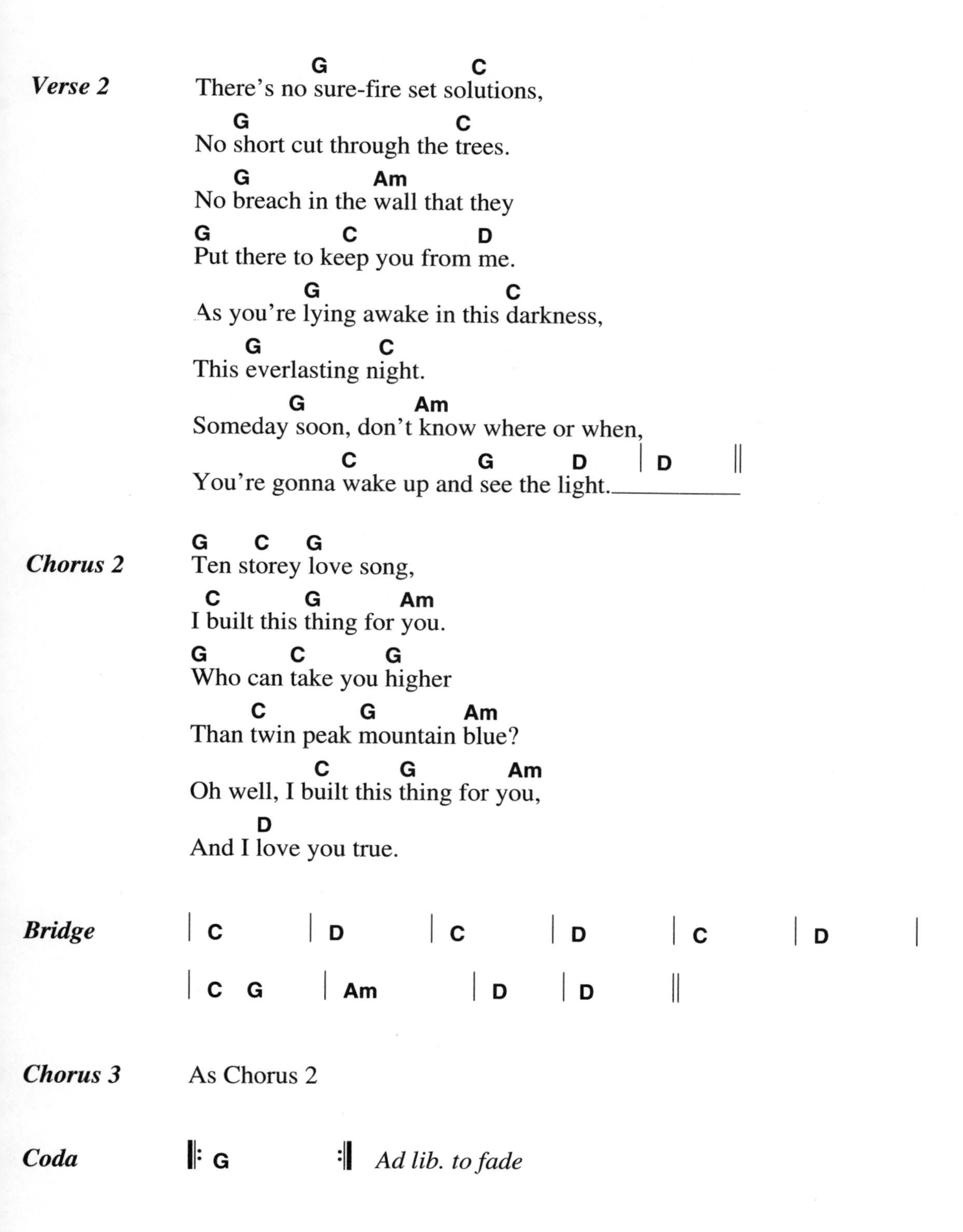
Verse 2
G C
There's no sure-fire set solutions,
G C
No short cut through the trees.
G Am
No breach in the wall that they
G C D
Put there to keep you from me.
G C
As you're lying awake in this darkness,
G C
This everlasting night.
G Am
Someday soon, don't know where or when,
C G D | D ||
You're gonna wake up and see the light.
Chorus 2
G C G
Ten storey love song,
C G Am
I built this thing for you.
G C G
Who can take you higher
C G Am
Than twin peak mountain blue?
C G Am
Oh well, I built this thing for you,
D
And I love you true.
Bridge
| C | D | C | D | C | D |
| C G | Am | D | D ||
Chorus 3
As Chorus 2
Coda
|: G :| Ad lib. to fade

There Is A Light That Never Goes Out

Words by Morrissey
Music by Johnny Marr

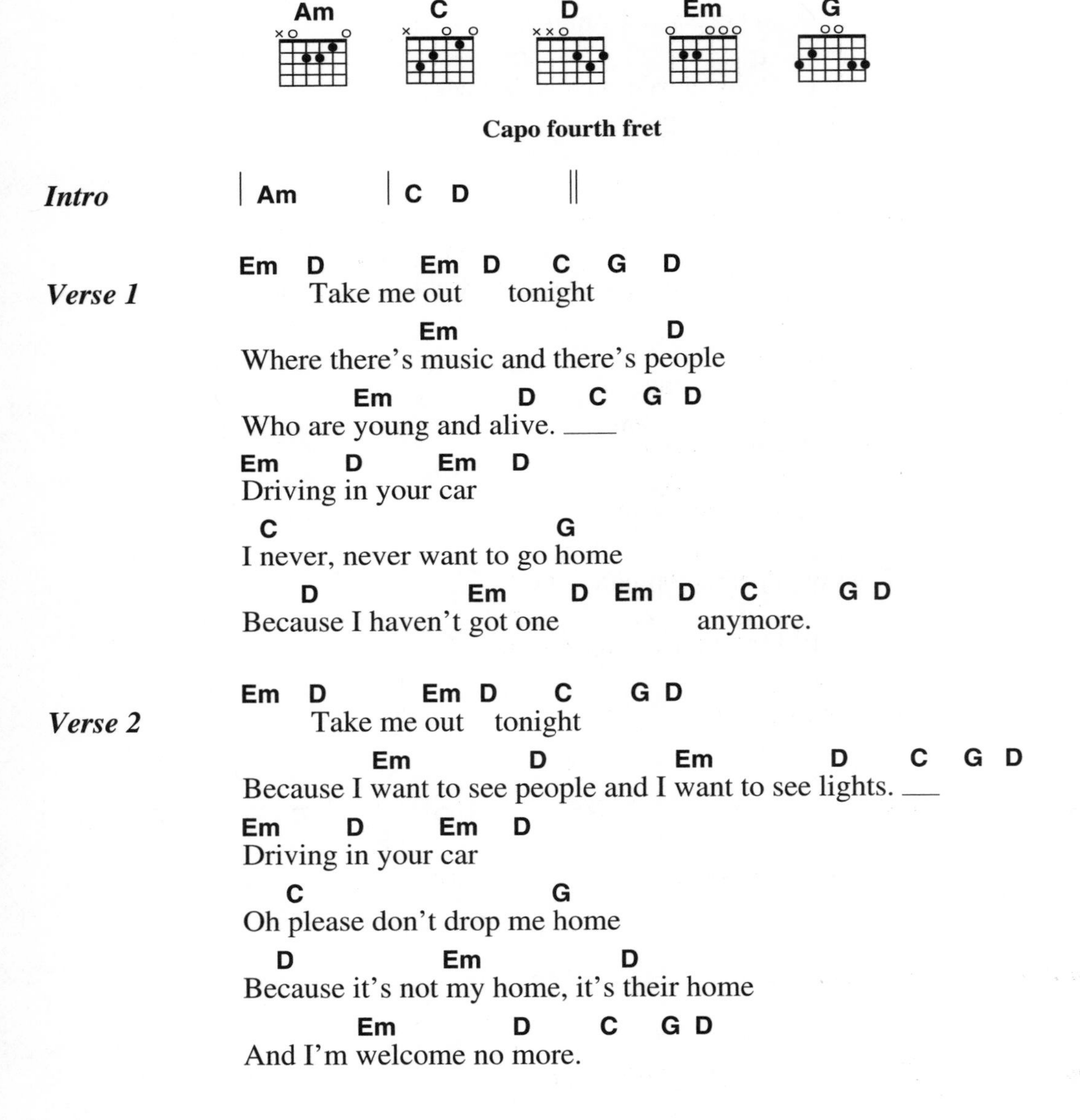

Capo fourth fret

Intro | Am | C D ||

Verse 1

Em D Em D C G D
Take me out tonight
Em D
Where there's music and there's people
Em D C G D
Who are young and alive. ___
Em D Em D
Driving in your car
C G
I never, never want to go home
D Em D Em D C G D
Because I haven't got one anymore.

Verse 2

Em D Em D C G D
Take me out tonight
Em D Em D C G D
Because I want to see people and I want to see lights. ___
Em D Em D
Driving in your car
C G
Oh please don't drop me home
D Em D
Because it's not my home, it's their home
Em D C G D
And I'm welcome no more.

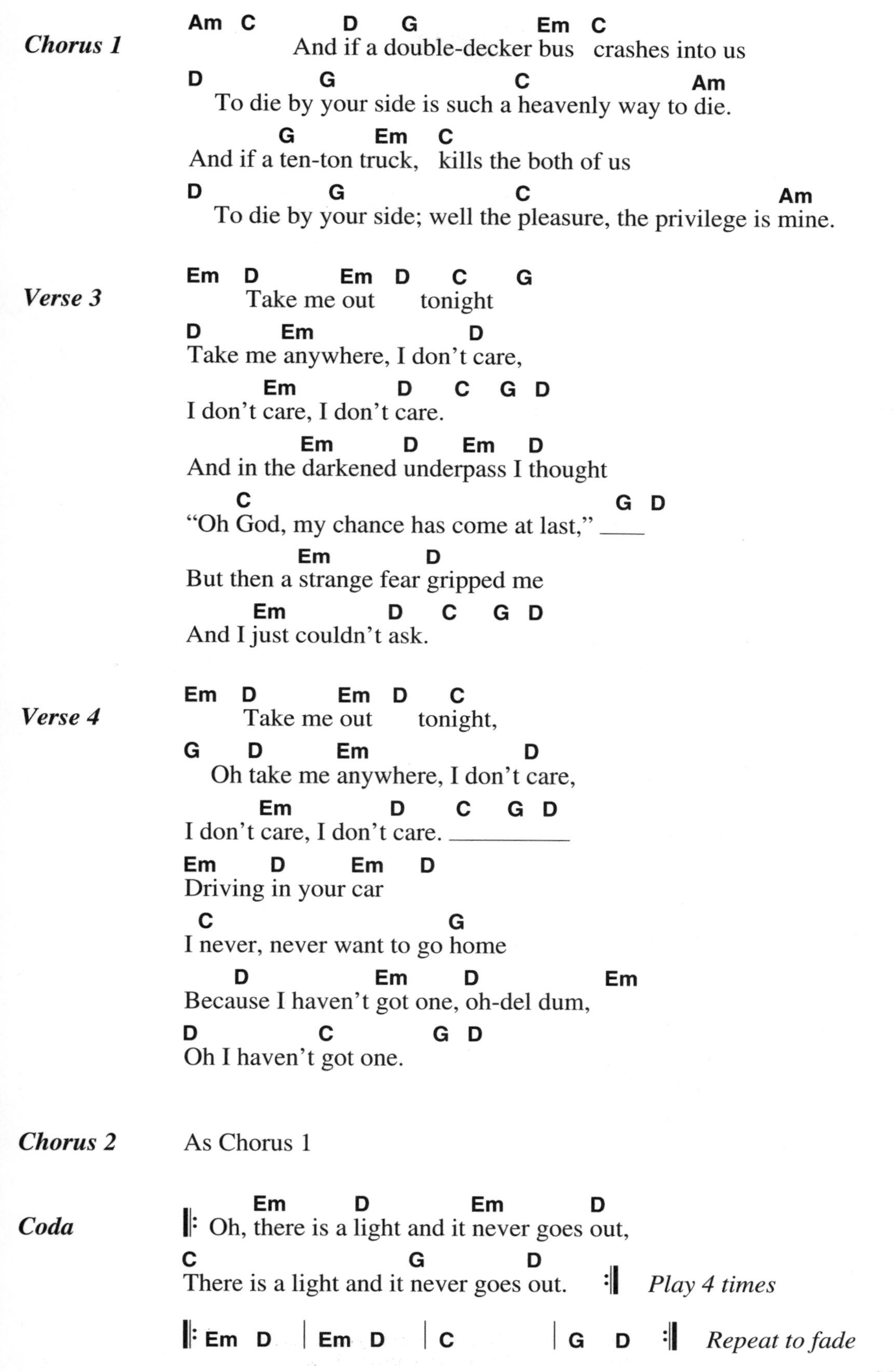

Chorus 1

Am C D G Em C
And if a double-decker bus crashes into us
D G C Am
To die by your side is such a heavenly way to die.
G Em C
And if a ten-ton truck, kills the both of us
D G C Am
To die by your side; well the pleasure, the privilege is mine.

Verse 3

Em D Em D C G
Take me out tonight
D Em D
Take me anywhere, I don't care,
Em D C G D
I don't care, I don't care.
Em D Em D
And in the darkened underpass I thought
C G D
"Oh God, my chance has come at last," ___
Em D
But then a strange fear gripped me
Em D C G D
And I just couldn't ask.

Verse 4

Em D Em D C
Take me out tonight,
G D Em D
Oh take me anywhere, I don't care,
Em D C G D
I don't care, I don't care. _________
Em D Em D
Driving in your car
C G
I never, never want to go home
D Em D Em
Because I haven't got one, oh-del dum,
D C G D
Oh I haven't got one.

Chorus 2 As Chorus 1

Coda

Em D Em D
‖: Oh, there is a light and it never goes out,
C G D
There is a light and it never goes out. :‖ *Play 4 times*

‖: Em D | Em D | C | G D :‖ *Repeat to fade*

Turn

Words & Music by
Fran Healy

G C D Am

Intro | G | G | G | G ||

Verse 1
```
G                               C
I want to see what people saw,
                             G
I want to feel like I felt  before.
G                                C
  I'd like to see the kingdom come,
                         D
I want to feel forever young.
```

Pre-chorus 1
```
G
  I want to sing,

To sing my song.
            D        C
I want to live in a world where I belong. __
Am
  I want to live,

I will survive,
                         D
And I believe that it won't be very long.
```

Chorus 1
```
       C     D
If we turn, turn, __
  G      C
Turn, turn, turn.
      D        G
Turn, turn, __ turn. __
```

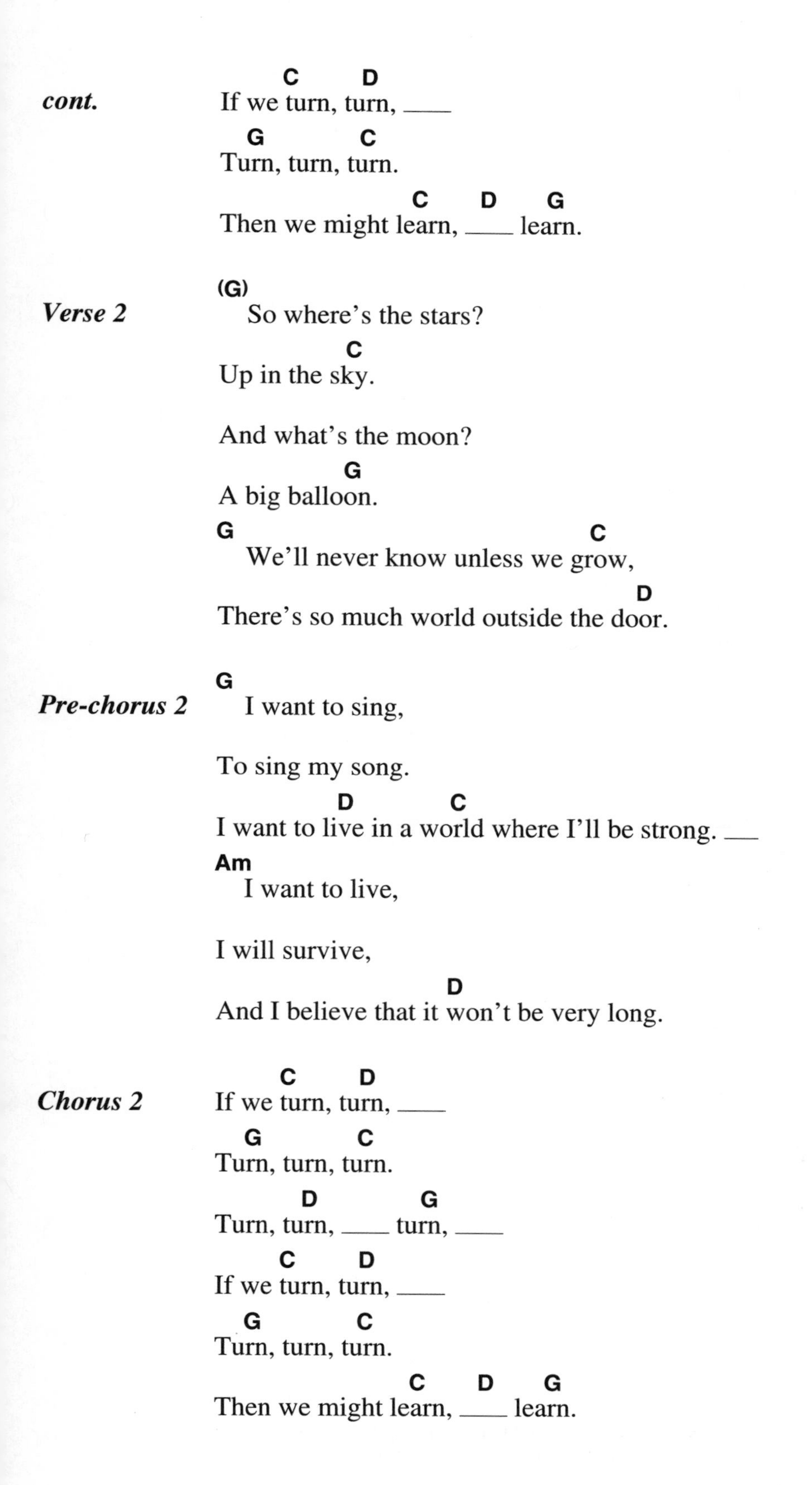

```
cont.         C     D
           If we turn, turn, ___
              G       C
           Turn, turn, turn.
                             C     D     G
           Then we might learn, ___ learn.

           (G)
Verse 2       So where's the stars?
                          C
           Up in the sky.

           And what's the moon?
                          G
           A big balloon.
           G                                    C
              We'll never know unless we grow,
                                                    D
           There's so much world outside the door.

           G
Pre-chorus 2  I want to sing,

           To sing my song.
                          D          C
           I want to live in a world where I'll be strong. ___
           Am
              I want to live,

           I will survive,
                                         D
           And I believe that it won't be very long.

                 C     D
Chorus 2   If we turn, turn, ___
              G       C
           Turn, turn, turn.
                   D         G
           Turn, turn, ___ turn, ___
                 C     D
           If we turn, turn, ___
              G       C
           Turn, turn, turn.
                             C     D     G
           Then we might learn, ___ learn.
```

Link

```
D
   We've got to turn, we've got to turn.

| C   D | G   C | C   D | G     ||
```

Chorus 3

```
      C      D
If we turn, turn, ___
  G        C
Turn, turn, turn.
        D        G
Turn, turn, ___ turn, ___
      C      D
If we turn, turn, ___
  G        C
Turn, turn, turn.
                 C
Then we might learn,
          D       G
Learn to turn. _____
```

Coda

```
|: G   | G   | G   | G   :|
```

Two Princes

Words & Music by
Chris Barron, Eric Schenkman, Mark White & Aaron Comess

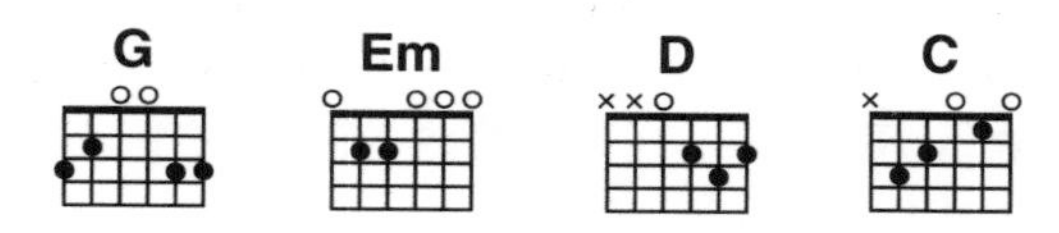

Capo second fret

Intro 1 bar drums ‖: G Em | D C | G Em | D C :‖

Verse 1
```
G            Em                D
One, two princes kneel before you,
        C
That's what I said, now.
G          Em              D
Princes, Princes, who adore you,
      C
Just go ahead, now.
G          Em              D
One has diamonds in his pocket
      C
And that's some bread now,
G                Em                  D
This one said he wants to buy you rockets,
       C
Ain't in his head, now.
```

Link 1 | G Em | D C | G Em | D C |

Verse 2
```
G            Em                D
This one, he got a princely racket,
        C
That's what I said, now.
G               Em            D
Got some big seal upon his jacket,
       C
Ain't in his head, now.
    G                Em          D
You marry him, your father will condone you,
```

```
              C
cont.         How 'bout that, now?
                  G                    Em           D
              You marry me, your father will disown you,
                   C
              He'll eat his hat, now.

              C
Pre-chorus 1  Marry him or marry me,
              G
              I'm the one that loves you baby can't you see?
                    C
              I ain't got no future or a family tree,
                  D
              But I know what a prince and lover ought to be,

              I know what a prince and lover ought to be.

                  G       Em                D
Chorus 1      Said, if you want to call me baby,
                  C
              Just go ahead, now.
                  G        Em                D
              An' if you'd like to tell me maybe,
                  C
              Just go ahead, now.
                  G       Em                D
              And if you wanna buy me flowers
                  C
              Just go ahead, now.
                  G       Em                D
              And if you like to talk for hours
                  C
              Just go ahead, now.


Guitar Solo   ||: G  Em | D  C | G  Em | D  C :|| C | G | C | D | D | D |

Verse 3       As Verse 1

Pre-chorus 2  As Pre-chorus 1
```

```
               G     N.C.
Chorus 2       Said, if you want to call me baby,

               Just go ahead, now.

               An' if you'd like to tell me maybe,

               Just go ahead, now.

               And if you wanna buy me flowers,

               Just go ahead, now.

               And if you like to talk for hours,

               Just go ahead, now.

               G     Em             D
Chorus 3       Said, if you want to call me baby,
                 C
               Just go ahead, now.
                 G                  D
               An' if you'd like to tell me maybe,
                 C
               Just go ahead, now.
                 G    Em            D
               And if you like to buy me flowers,
                 C
               Just go ahead, now.
                 G    Em            D
               And if you like to talk for hours
                 C
               Just go ahead, now.
```

Chorus 4 𝄆 As Chorus 1 𝄇 *Repeat to fade w/ad lib vocals*

Walk Of Life

Words & Music by
Mark Knopfler

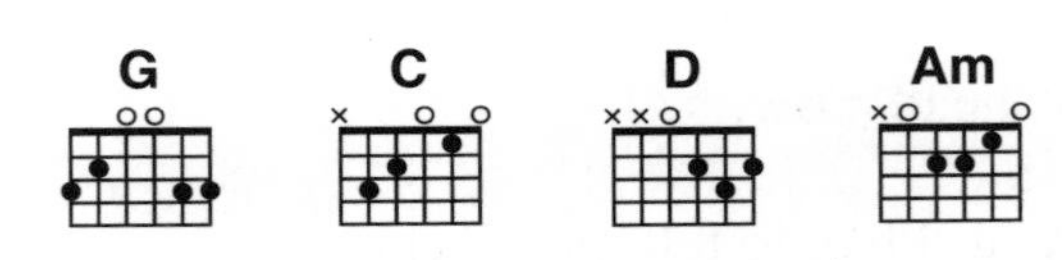

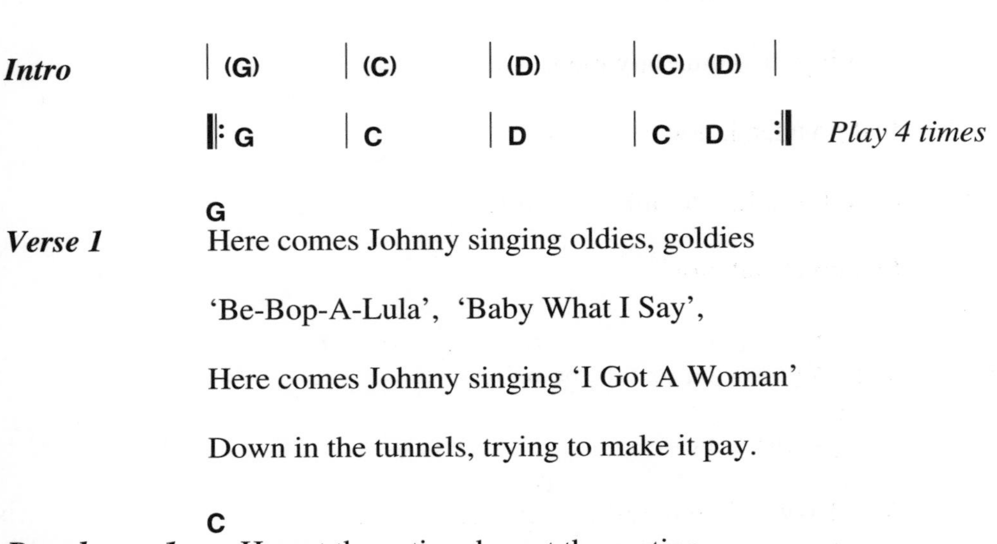

Intro

```
| (G)   | (C)   | (D)   | (C)  (D) |

|: G    | C     | D     | C    D  :|   Play 4 times
```

Verse 1

```
G
Here comes Johnny singing oldies, goldies

'Be-Bop-A-Lula', 'Baby What I Say',

Here comes Johnny singing 'I Got A Woman'

Down in the tunnels, trying to make it pay.
```

Pre-chorus 1

```
C
   He got the action, he got the motion
G
   Oh yeah, the boy can play.
C
   Dedication, devotion,
G
Turning all the night time into the day.
```

Chorus 1

```
             G                          D
He do the song about the sweet-lovin' woman,
             G                    C
He do the song about the knife,
             G     D                C     Am
He do the walk,   do the walk of life,
D
Yeah, he do the walk of (life.)
```

Link

```
| G     | C     | D     | C    D  ||
  life.
```

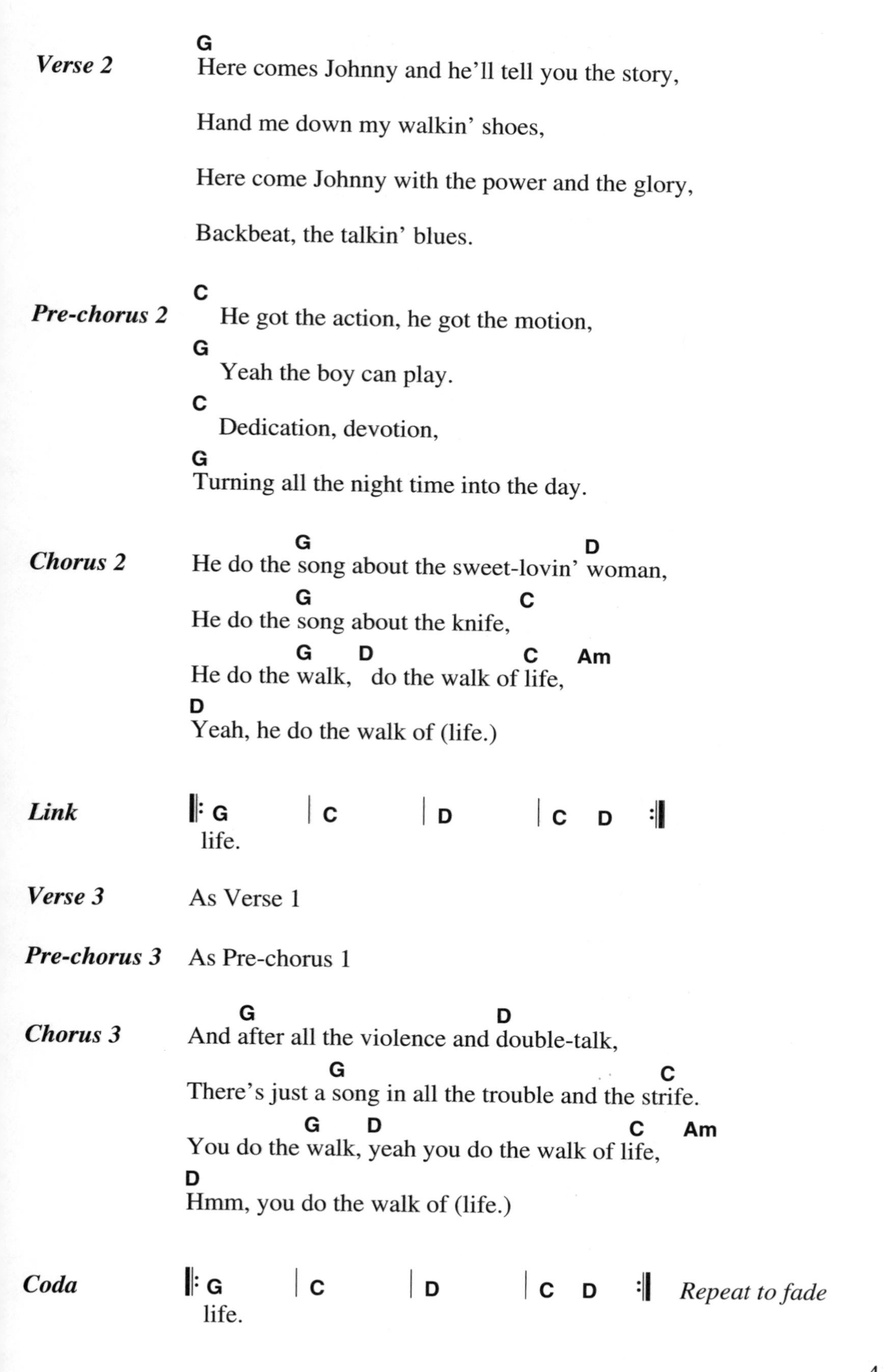

Verse 2

G
Here comes Johnny and he'll tell you the story,

Hand me down my walkin' shoes,

Here come Johnny with the power and the glory,

Backbeat, the talkin' blues.

Pre-chorus 2

C
He got the action, he got the motion,
G
Yeah the boy can play.
C
Dedication, devotion,
G
Turning all the night time into the day.

Chorus 2

G D
He do the song about the sweet-lovin' woman,
G C
He do the song about the knife,
G D C Am
He do the walk, do the walk of life,
D
Yeah, he do the walk of (life.)

Link

‖: G | C | D | C D :‖
life.

Verse 3 As Verse 1

Pre-chorus 3 As Pre-chorus 1

Chorus 3

G D
And after all the violence and double-talk,
G C
There's just a song in all the trouble and the strife.
G D C Am
You do the walk, yeah you do the walk of life,
D
Hmm, you do the walk of (life.)

Coda

‖: G | C | D | C D :‖ *Repeat to fade*
life.

What's Up

Words & Music by
Linda Perry

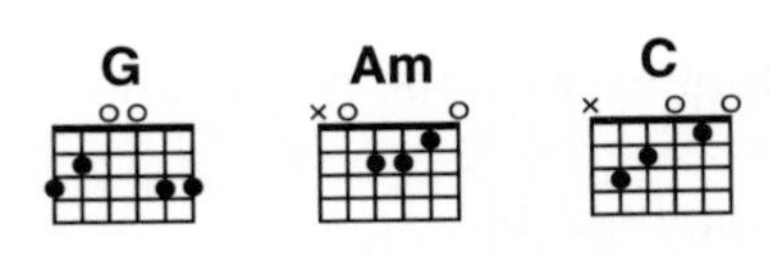

Capo second fret

Intro | G | Am | C | G | G | Am | C | G |

Verse 1

G
25 years and my life and still
Am C
I'm trying to get up that great big hill of hope
G
For a destination.

And I realised quickly when I knew I should
Am
That the world was made up of this
C
Brotherhood of man,
G
For whatever that means.

Pre-chorus 1

G
And so I cry sometimes when I'm lying in bed
Am
Just to get it all out, what's in my head
C G
And I, I am feeling a little peculiar.

And so I wake in the morning and I step
Am
Outside and I take a deep breath

And I get real high
C
And I scream from the top of my lungs,
G
"What's goin' on?"

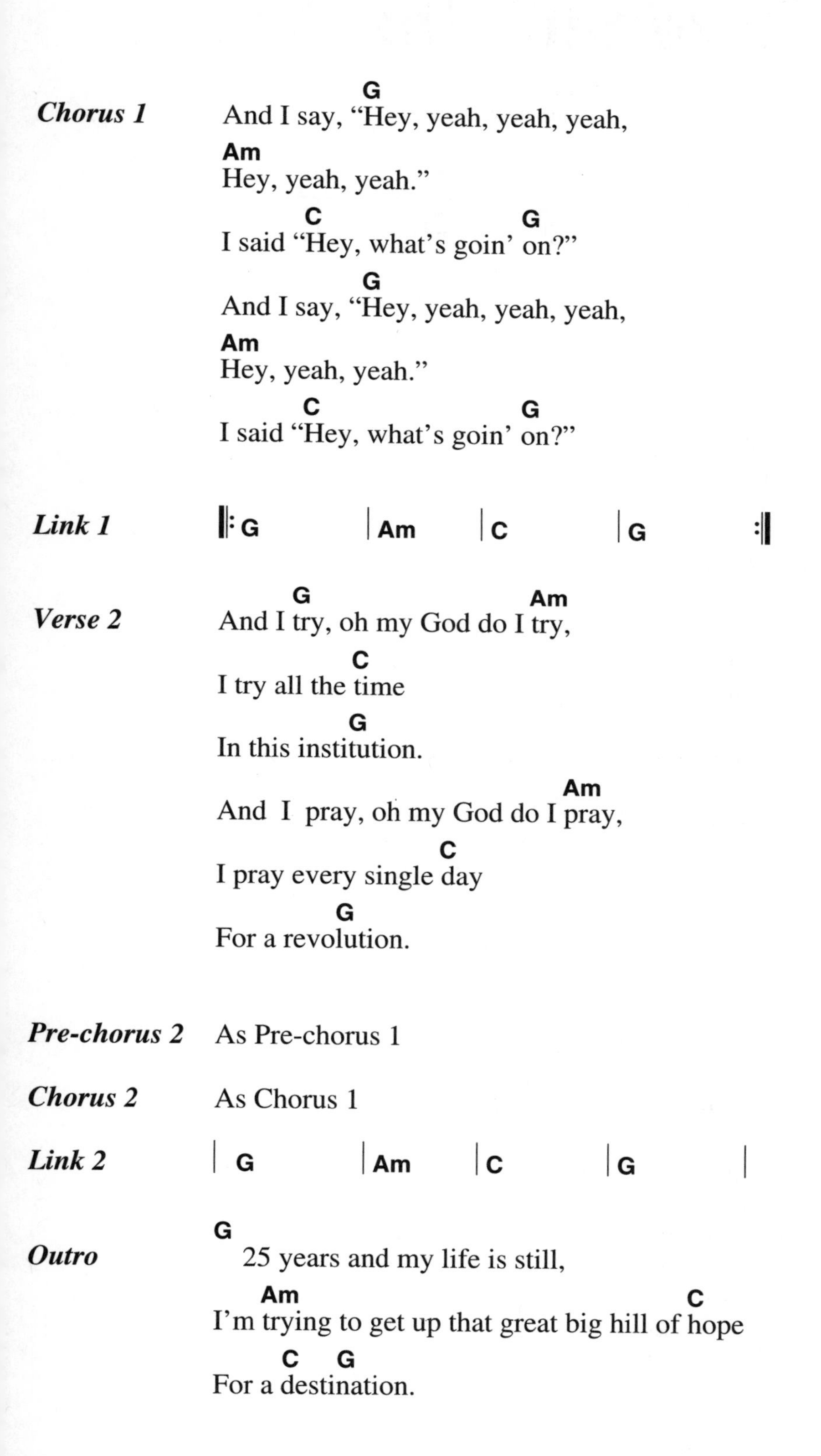

```
Chorus 1        G
        And I say, "Hey, yeah, yeah, yeah,
        Am
        Hey, yeah, yeah."
             C               G
        I said "Hey, what's goin' on?"
                        G
        And I say, "Hey, yeah, yeah, yeah,
        Am
        Hey, yeah, yeah."
             C               G
        I said "Hey, what's goin' on?"

Link 1  ||: G        | Am      | C        | G        :||

                G                    Am
Verse 2 And I try, oh my God do I try,
                     C
        I try all the time
                     G
        In this institution.
                                     Am
        And  I  pray, oh my God do I pray,
                               C
        I pray every single day
                    G
        For a revolution.

Pre-chorus 2  As Pre-chorus 1

Chorus 2      As Chorus 1

Link 2  |  G        | Am      | C        | G        |

        G
Outro     25 years and my life is still,
           Am                                      C
        I'm trying to get up that great big hill of hope
               C   G
        For a destination.
```

You're Still The One

Words & Music by
Shania Twain & R.J. Lange

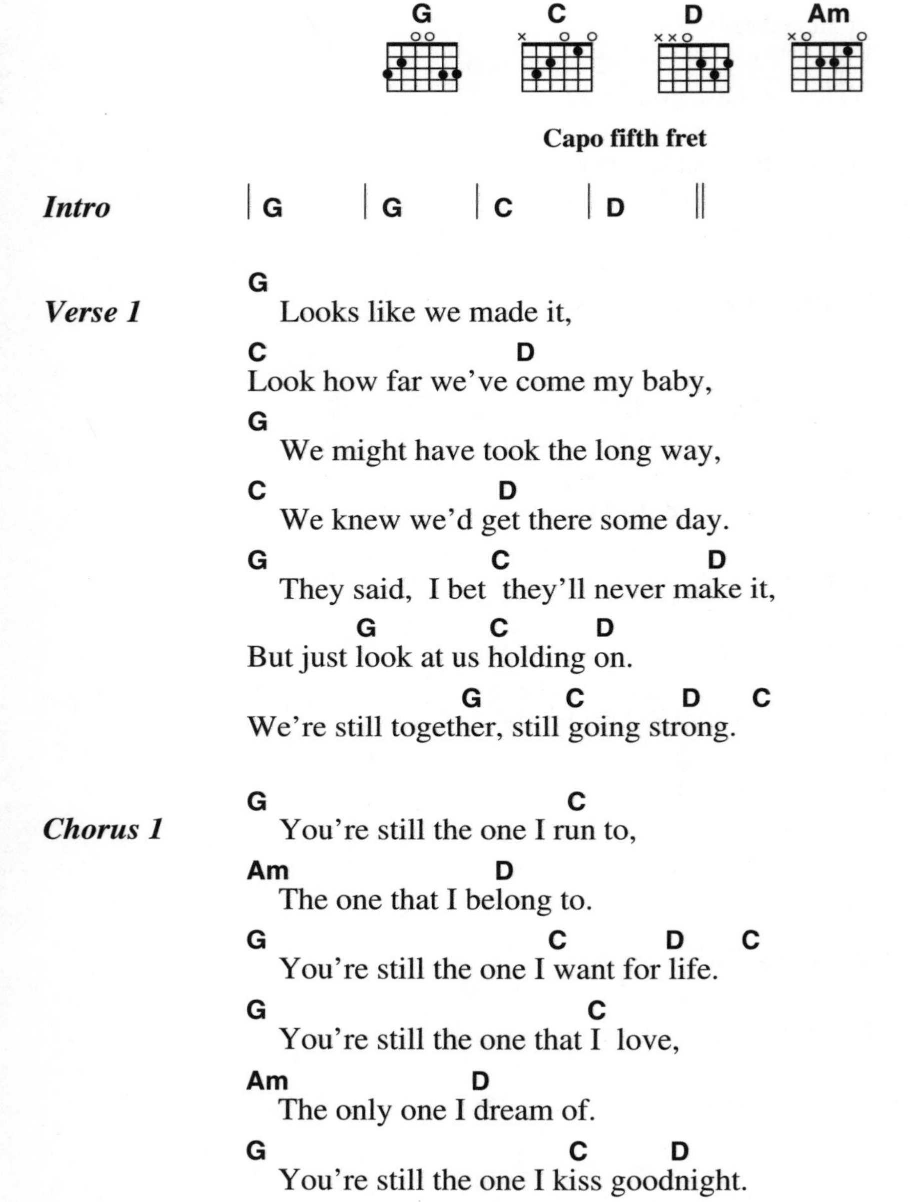

Capo fifth fret

Intro | G | G | C | D ||

Verse 1

```
G
  Looks like we made it,
C                   D
Look how far we've come my baby,
G
  We might have took the long way,
C                D
  We knew we'd get there some day.
G                    C                 D
  They said,  I bet  they'll never make it,
           G         C        D
But just look at us holding on.
                  G         C          D      C
We're still together, still going strong.
```

Chorus 1

```
G                            C
  You're still the one I run to,
Am                  D
  The one that I belong to.
G                        C          D      C
  You're still the one I want for life.
G                              C
  You're still the one that I  love,
Am               D
  The only one I dream of.
G                          C          D
  You're still the one I kiss goodnight.
```

```
              G
Verse 2         Ain't nothing better,
              C          D
               We beat the odds together.
              G
                I'm glad we didn't listen,
              C                 D
              Look at what we would be missing.
              G              C             D
                They said,  I bet  they'll never make it,
                    G      C     D
              But just look at us holding on.
                         G       C      D
              We're still together, still going strong.

              G                    C
Chorus 2        You're still the one I run to,
              Am                 D
                The one that I belong to.
              G                   C       D    C
                You're still the one I want for life.
              G                      C
                You're still the one that I  love,
              Am               D
                The only one I dream of.
              G                    C      D
                You're still the one I kiss goodnight.

              You're still the one.

Instrumental  ||: G      | C       | D       | D       :||

              G                    C
Chorus 3        You're still the one I run to,
              Am                 D
                The one that I belong to.
              G                   C       D    C
                You're still the one I want for life.
              G                      C
                You're still the one that I  love,
              Am               D
                The only one I dream of.
              G                    C      D
                You're still the one I kiss goodnight.
              G
                I'm so glad we made it,
              C                 D
              Look how far we've come baby.
```

You Can Call Me Al

Words & Music by
Paul Simon

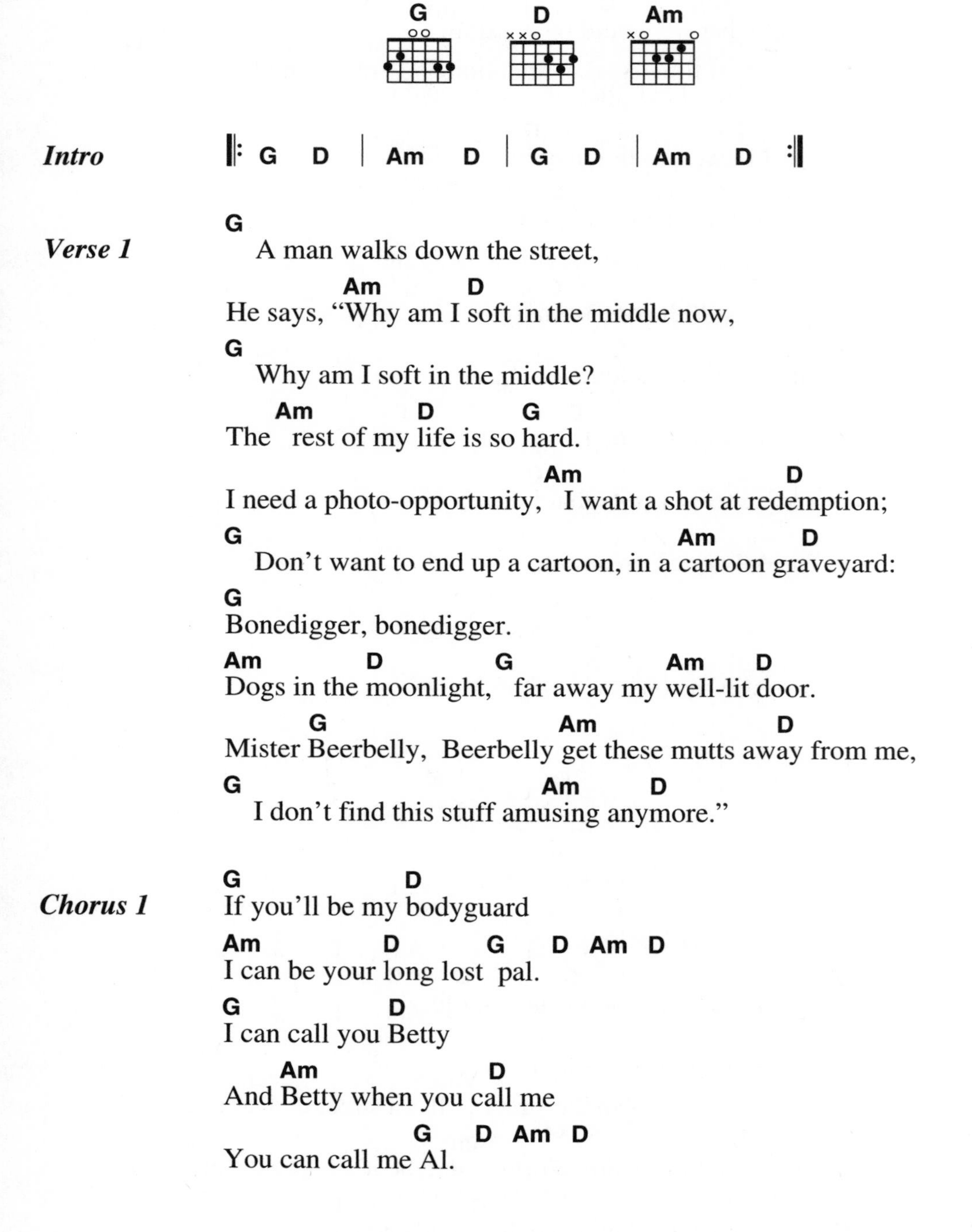

```
            G         D         Am

Intro      |: G    D | Am    D | G    D | Am    D :|

           G
Verse 1       A man walks down the street,
                    Am          D
           He says, "Why am I soft in the middle now,
           G
              Why am I soft in the middle?
               Am            D        G
           The   rest of my life is so hard.
                                         Am                      D
           I need a photo-opportunity,   I want a shot at redemption;
           G                                          Am          D
              Don't want to end up a cartoon, in a cartoon graveyard:
           G
           Bonedigger, bonedigger.
           Am             D             G              Am       D
           Dogs in the moonlight,   far away my well-lit door.
                    G                       Am                    D
           Mister Beerbelly,  Beerbelly get these mutts away from me,
           G                                 Am        D
              I don't find this stuff amusing anymore."

           G               D
Chorus 1   If you'll be my bodyguard
           Am              D           G      D  Am  D
           I can be your long lost  pal.
           G               D
           I can call you Betty
                Am                 D
           And Betty when you call me
                               G     D  Am  D
           You can call me Al.
```

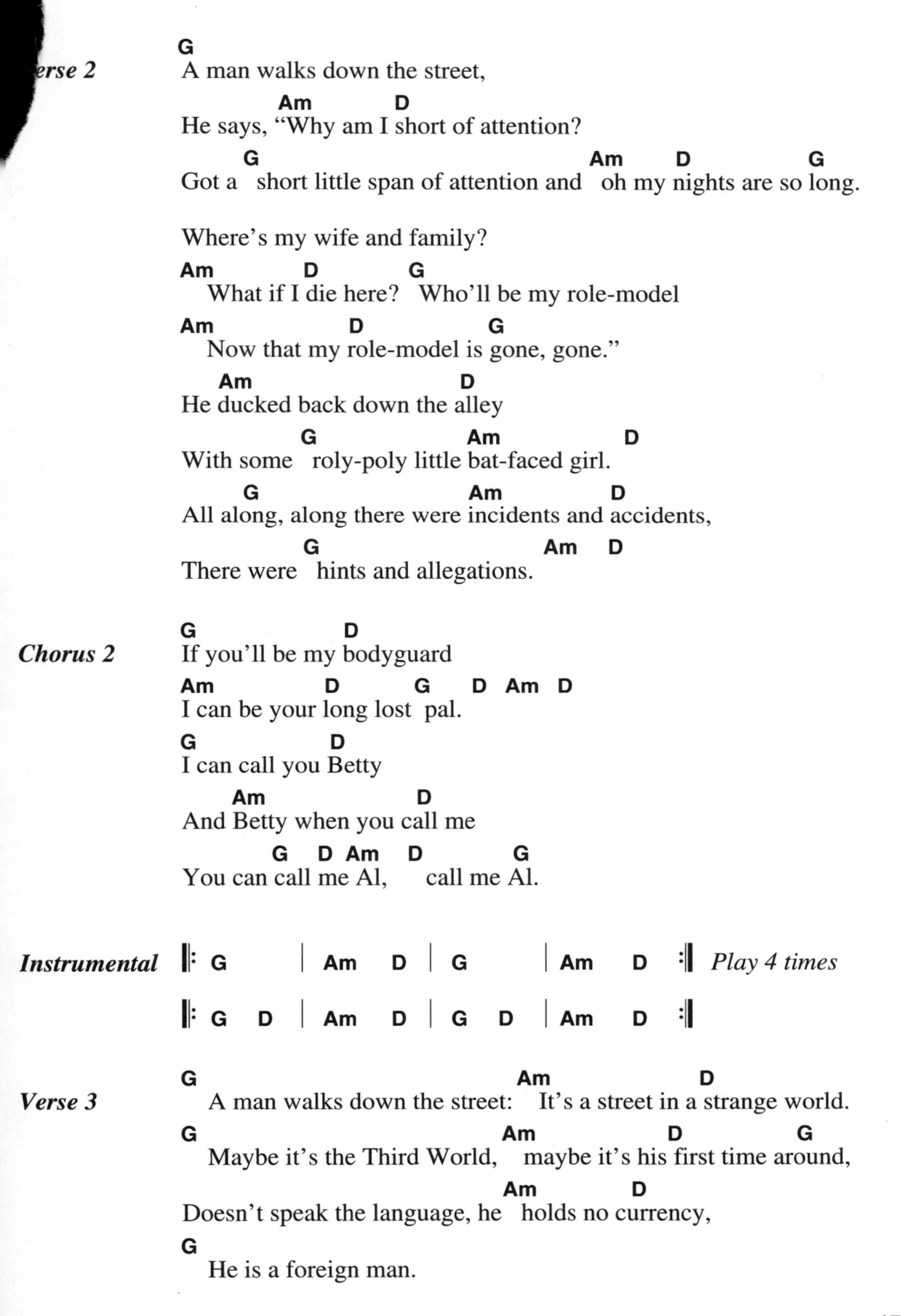
G
erse 2 A man walks down the street,
Am D
He says, "Why am I short of attention?
G Am D G
Got a short little span of attention and oh my nights are so long.
Where's my wife and family?
Am D G
What if I die here? Who'll be my role-model
Am D G
Now that my role-model is gone, gone."
Am D
He ducked back down the alley
G Am D
With some roly-poly little bat-faced girl.
G Am D
All along, along there were incidents and accidents,
G Am D
There were hints and allegations.
G D
Chorus 2 If you'll be my bodyguard
Am D G D Am D
I can be your long lost pal.
G D
I can call you Betty
Am D
And Betty when you call me
G D Am D G
You can call me Al, call me Al.
Instrumental ‖: G | Am D | G | Am D :‖ Play 4 times
‖: G D | Am D | G D | Am D :‖
G Am D
Verse 3 A man walks down the street: It's a street in a strange world.
G Am D G
Maybe it's the Third World, maybe it's his first time around,
Am D
Doesn't speak the language, he holds no currency,
G
He is a foreign man.

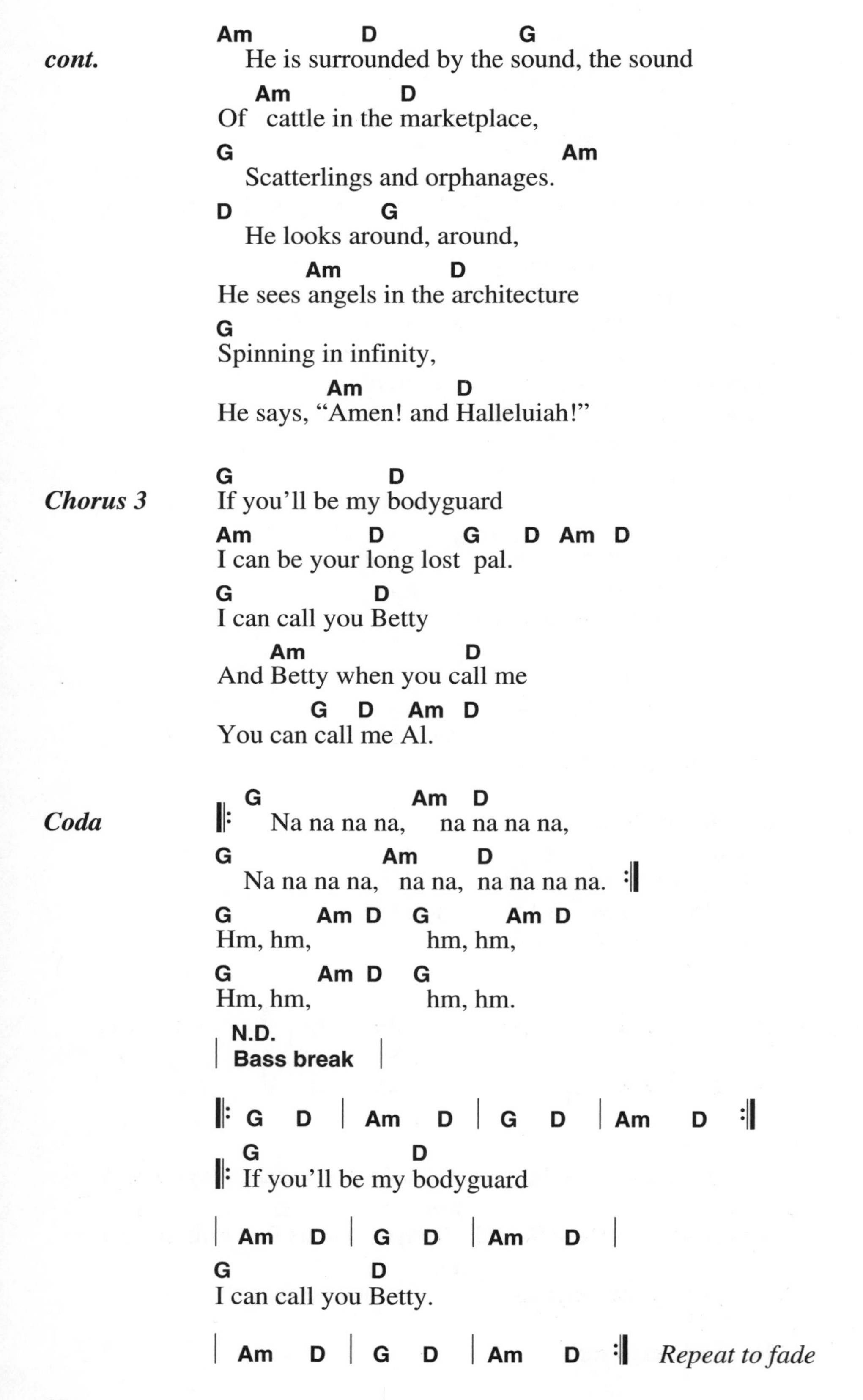

cont.

Am D G
He is surrounded by the sound, the sound
Am D
Of cattle in the marketplace,
G Am
Scatterlings and orphanages.
D G
He looks around, around,
Am D
He sees angels in the architecture
G
Spinning in infinity,
Am D
He says, "Amen! and Halleluiah!"

Chorus 3

G D
If you'll be my bodyguard
Am D G D Am D
I can be your long lost pal.
G D
I can call you Betty
Am D
And Betty when you call me
G D Am D
You can call me Al.

Coda

𝄆 G Am D
Na na na na, na na na na,
G Am D
Na na na na, na na, na na na na. 𝄇
G Am D G Am D
Hm, hm, hm, hm,
G Am D G
Hm, hm, hm, hm.

| N.D. Bass break |

𝄆 G D | Am D | G D | Am D 𝄇

G D
𝄆 If you'll be my bodyguard

| Am D | G D | Am D |

G D
I can call you Betty.

| Am D | G D | Am D 𝄇 *Repeat to fade*

11/05(56830)